MW00563153

"Samuel Avery gives us a refresh[ingly] written account of Reality, ripe with clarity and larger than scientific or religious narratives have yet to grasp. I enjoyed this highly original and deeply insightful look into the essence of consciousness and its relationships with the worlds of physics and biology."

—**Allan Combs**, PhD, President of The Society for Consciousness Studies, and award-winning author of *The Radiance of Being* and *Consciousness Explained Better*

"Sam Avery is one of the pioneers of the 'observer creating reality' solution to the relationship between mind and matter as described in quantum physics. Here he presents a new method for the reader to envision this relationship with more clarity."

—**Fred Alan Wolf**, PhD, Quantum Physicist, author of many books including *Time-Loops and Space-Twists: How God Created the Universe* and *Dr. Quantum's Little Book of Big Ideas*

"While a number of physicists and philosophers have explored the relationship between the insights of Eastern meditation traditions and the revelations of modern physics, Mr. Avery is the first to create a new epistemology that fully integrates the insights of both disciplines."

—**Charles Lynd**, Media Ecologist, The Ohio State University College of Education and Human Ecology (retired)

"Samuel Avery's concept of the dimensional structure of consciousness is brilliant and paradigm-shattering. Once you get it, you'll never see the world in quite the same way again; it will all make so much more sense. In Part II of *The Quantum Screen*, he's introduced himself more personally and explained the ethical and ecological implications of understanding the world as a living experience of consciousness."

—**Toby Johnson**, author of *Finding Your Own True Myth: What I Learned from Joseph Campbell*

THE QUANTUM SCREEN

THE ENIGMAS OF MODERN PHYSICS AND A NEW MODEL OF PERCEPTUAL CONSCIOUSNESS

SAMUEL AVERY

Wetware Media, LLC

ALSO BY SAMUEL AVERY

A Note to the Reader

We are excited that you are about to dive into Samuel Avery's exceptional book, *The Quantum Screen*, which presents an entirely new paradigm that sheds fresh light on consciousness, one of the deepest human mysteries.

Avery is a unique and rigorous thinker, and he references aspects of physics to illustrate his reasoning. While you do not need to understand the theorems he shares to fully appreciate his message, we encourage you to try to explore the physics presented if you are not already versed in the topic.

If you find it would be helpful to have a more graphic and pictorial explanation of the ideas in this book, we have also published *Dimensions Within: Physics and the Structure of Consciousness*, an interactive audio-visual book created by Avery. This interactive book uses a combination of written text, animated videos, talking videos, and audio to provide a detailed, step-by-step explanation of the physics supporting his model of consciousness.

Dimensions Within: Physics and the Structure of Consciousness is available for Kindle devices at amazon.com and for iOS devices in the Apple® iBooks® store.

We appreciate your interest in Avery's groundbreaking work, and hope you enjoy reading *The Quantum Screen*.

CONTENTS

FOREWORD

Samuel Avery is one of those rare individuals who change the world by discovering something about how it works and sharing that discovery with all of us. He has been thinking and writing about consciousness for many years and, with each new book he writes, his thinking becomes more refined. In *The Quantum Screen*, his most recent offering, Sam covers tremendous intellectual ground—brilliantly combining physics and a spiritual view of consciousness. As with his other books, Sam insists on including the physics that support his theory regarding the dimensional structure of consciousness. In this book, he makes an extra effort to explain the direct linkage between physics and consciousness.

My experience with Sam reminds me of the Buddhist aphorism, "When the student is ready, the master appears." I began an email correspondence with Sam after discovering two of his early books, *The Dimensional Structure of Consciousness* and *Transcendence of the Western Mind*, which I found inspiring, challenging and wholly unique. While writing his next book, *Buddha and the Quantum*, he invited me to participate in an on-line group that would review and comment on his writing. I had the great fortune to spend time with him in person while he was touring the west coast to promote *Buddha and the Quantum*. I invited him to my home while he was passing through southern California. We broke bread together and spent quality time sitting in my back yard sipping good Kentucky bourbon and smoking fine cigars. We talked late into the night about the connection between physics and consciousness. It was an enjoyable and mind-expanding visit.

Although Sam is unassuming in person, he is one of our foremost thinkers on consciousness. He asks us to consider an alternative way of looking at things we thought we understood. Before Copernicus, we believed the earth was the center of the universe. Now we know better. Before Einstein, we believed energy and mass were separate and distinct aspects of the universe.

However, with his famous equation E=mc2, we've come to understand that they are not only the same, but inter-changeable. Before reading *The Quantum Screen*, you may imagine that science and spiritual matters are separate entities. After reading, you will likely have an entirely different perspective.

I sincerely believe that history will place Sam alongside the likes of Copernicus and Einstein. It has been a pleasure to watch his thinking evolve to the razor point on display in *The Quantum Screen*.

When Sam Avery came to my house several years ago, it marked a turning point in my intellectual life. Now, with *The Quantum Screen*, Sam is knocking at your door. It's your turn to invite the master into your home. This book will expand your mind and broaden your understanding not only of what consciousness is, but how it works.

Read it and be changed forever.

STEPHEN HAGE

Stephen Hage is the author of *Let There Be Light: Physics, Philosophy & The Dimensional Structure of Consciousness*. He is an expert in radiology, a regular contributor to technical journals, and a lecturer and instructor. Perhaps most revealing of the questions that drive his inquisitive mind is the title of his first published journal article, *Visualizing the Invisible*.

How This Book is Organized

Here is an overview of the chapters in Part I, followed by a brief explanation of Part II.

Part I: The Quantum Screen

Each topic in Part I is introduced in sequence, though all are organically interrelated. Each is fully understandable only in interaction with other topics, and only in the context of the whole. Each topic focuses on the central concept of the quantum screen.

Chapter 1 describes what the quantum screen is, how it works, where it comes from, and how it contrasts with "the Box."

Chapter 2 presents a guided meditation in which I show where the elements of consciousness come from and how they are put together to compose the quantum screen. The Screen is not just an idea. It is not something we only think about. It is something we see and experience in everyday life. I hope to present the Screen in such a way that anyone can experience it directly and immediately.

Chapter 3 focuses on physics. Quantum mechanics and relativity theory create the necessity for a new model of perceptual consciousness. Modern physics has discovered that space and time are not the rigid structural beams and rafters of the physical world they were thought to be. A totally new understanding of the relationship between consciousness and the world is now required. Some readers not trained in the particulars of physics may find this chapter more challenging than the others, but I hope to be able to present it in a friendly manner. We can all benefit from learning a bit more in this often-challenging discipline.

Chapter 4 discusses the evolution of consciousness. Here I present three levels of consciousness—the *cellular*, the *organic*, and the *organizational*—and the evolutionary process by which each proceeds to the next. Knowing how each level is built of components from the next lower level is essential to understanding the composite structure of consciousness. The whole is a composite—it consists of its parts—but becomes a full reality transcending the sum of its parts.

Chapter 5 I call *Self and Doing*. Thus far, the Screen may seem to be too passive a model, as if consciousness were something one merely watches, like television. But with the introduction of a non-perceptual realm, the Screen becomes interactive. This is where the *self* comes in. We do things; we rearrange objects in space in time. The self is not consciousness; it is part of consciousness—an organizing principle. It is the focus of order necessary to bring what we think into the physical. Bringing conceptual consciousness into the physical dimensions is what *doing* is.

Chapter 6 presents collective consciousness. Collective consciousness is the level of consciousness over and above the individual organism. I introduce a new realm of consciousness, the *observational* realm. Through the observational realm, one becomes aware of a much larger world, a world too big to be perceived in its entirety by separate individuals.

Chapter 7 explains why this model is more than an academic exercise. As humanity transforms itself into a new form of life, it assumes a new identity, hopefully one that incorporates new discoveries in physics and biology.

Part II: Related Essays

Part II is a series of essays related to the quantum screen model. They include:
   • An autobiography
   • A discussion of energy policy
   • A philosophical dialogue based on the work of George Berkeley
   • A presentation on near-death experience

I include these to illustrate the wide-ranging implications of a non-dualistic understanding of physical reality.

THE QUANTUM SCREEN

PART I

Science cannot solve the ultimate mystery of nature.
And that is because, in the last analysis, we ourselves
are a part of the mystery that we are trying to solve.

— Max Planck

INTRODUCTION

What is the connection between physics and consciousness?

At first glance they appear to be polar opposites. Physics is concrete and verifiable; consciousness is mysterious and subjective. Physics can be demonstrated; consciousness cannot. Both physics and consciousness are real, but there seems to be no connection between them. This produces a duality: two truths, both valid, without any apparent connection. The duality is a division between spirit and matter, between mind and body, between religion and science—the essential neurosis at the core of our civilization. As a society, we have never resolved the difference between what we experience in consciousness and what we think actually exists in the world.

Growing up with two scientist parents who attended church regularly, I am familiar with this dualism. At an early age, I developed a scientific mentality and thought that I would likely become a scientist in adulthood. In college, however, I found myself looking for deeper meaning than science could offer. Science could tell us how things worked, but not what they were. I wanted to know what they were. I began practicing a form of meditation without realizing that it was meditation. Fascination with what I was seeing lead to studying the spiritual traditions in which meditation developed. But my interest in science never waned, and I retained a scientifically based skepticism toward spiritual experience. I did not believe things easily.

Throughout early adulthood I was keenly aware of the tension between science and religion. In time, I came to suspect that the two modalities were fundamentally connected and possibly linked through the dimensions of space, time, and mass. I suspected that the relationship between spirituality and science, or between consciousness and the physical world, might have something to do with the dimensions: Time, space and mass.

In the Western tradition we reduce just about everything to material substance, to things verified through mechanical processes, that is, to cause and effect. We even try to understand consciousness as a complexity of material processes—as an intricacy of chemical reactions or electrical interactions. But this does not work, because it overlooks the fact that something must be experiencing the process. There has to be some kind of presence beneath the structure we know as science. I began to realize the objectivity underlying science was not as fundamental as some other presence, something not easily seen.

The Enigmas of Modern Physics

But I was never satisfied with flowery esoteric descriptions of religious experience that supposedly underlie the oneness of life. I wanted a scientifically rigorous proof of an underlying oneness. Physicists, I remembered, were having trouble with dimensions. Relativity theory and quantum mechanics seem to get themselves into places where space contracts, time slows down, and mass increases. Space, time, and mass also seem to collapse into one another in subatomic particles. Light, meanwhile, has momentum but no mass and is subject to no time dimension at all. These are all very weird phenomena. Though part of science, they make no sense from the scientific perspective. I call them the enigmas of modern physics. One day I realized that all of the enigmas have something very interesting in common. They all involve the "role of the observer." What does that mean? What is the role of the observer? It's consciousness! What else? There has to be somebody looking at what is happening! All of the enigmas of modern physics have to do with space, time, and mass, and with consciousness.

The enigmas are imperceptible in everyday life because they occur only at dimensional extremes: the very distant, the very small, the very fast, or the very massive, such as in the vicinity of a black hole. In other words, the enigmas appear at the extreme edges of the dimensional world. My epiphany came when I realized that if you take consciousness outside of the dimensions, turn things around, and put the dimensions back inside consciousness, you have a whole new picture, a non-dualistic picture. Then I looked to see if the dimensions might serve as fundamental structures of consciousness. Why do we think we are in space? How do we "move through" space? My idea to put the dimensions inside consciousness sounded strange, because we normally think of consciousness as completely unstructured—a strange fluid of some sort sloshing around in our brains. We don't think of consciousness as something we can look at or analyze in any way. So in order to develop this picture, to look more deeply into this inside-out theory, I needed to look directly at consciousness itself.

What are the aspects of consciousness? What are its features? Are there separate realms of consciousness? Seeing is very different from hearing, and thinking from smelling. Imagining is very different from tasting. Each is a separate and qualitatively distinct form of experience, yet there is an underlying unity. How, specifically, are these separate realms of consciousness interrelated? How do they interact with each other to create the picture we call the physical world?

I began looking at the world from a completely different angle. The model I eventually adopted as a representation of perceptual consciousness and of the world—a model I call the quantum screen—is somewhat like the pixel screen of a computer or television. The Screen is not in space; space is in the Screen. The Screen is what you are looking at! The traditional way of viewing the world, with consciousness inside the dimensions, I call the Box. I was thinking outside the box!

The Box is the commonsense view of consciousness and dimensions. It consists of a space and time universe, with us in it. We are inside the Box. Not only are we inside, everything real has to be inside the Box. If something is not in the box, you can't see it. You can't deal with it. You can't measure it. So, if you want me to see a particular thing, you have to point to it and show me where it is in the Box. Then I can verify that it is actually there. If you can't do that, I don't know whether it is real or not. The box works well for everyday life, but does not work when we try to put consciousness inside it. That's when problems begin. The problems are not metaphysical, they are physical—physicists themselves have trouble understanding what happens to dimensions as observers come closer and closer to dimensional extremes. But I was never a physicist; I had no suggestions for changing what physicists were looking at. I was only suggesting an entirely new way to look at the same thing.

A Paradigm Shift

The classic paradigm shift is an example of a new way to look at the same thing. When you look at the planets and stars and moon on a clear night, you are looking at the same sky the ancient Greeks and Babylonians saw thousands of years ago. The sky we see now is the same sky the pre-Copernicans saw. The difference—the only difference—is in where we are looking from. We understand ourselves to be viewing the night sky from a moving platform. The weird back and forth motions of the planets are due not to their inherent weirdness, as was previously thought, but to our own motion around the sun. Things make better sense this way. Copernicus didn't change anything about what people saw; he changed how they saw it. This revolutionized understanding of our place in the universe. It changed us. A paradigm shift changes our point of view; a big paradigm shift changes who we think we are.

The Screen that I use as a model of consciousness is similar to a computer or television screen except that, whereas a pixel screen has two dimensions of space, the quantum screen, like a hologram, has three. (It also has two dimensions of time, but we will get to that later.) With the Screen, consciousness is non-dualistic. That is, there is no separation between the seer and the seen. There is nothing behind the Screen. There is only the image we see. That's it. That's the full extent of physical reality. There is no world "out there" separate from the seeing—no duality. The Screen is immediate: right here, right now, but the Screen is also immediate in the sense that there is nothing between us and that which we experience. There is no seer and no seen. There is only the seeing. Empty perceptual consciousness is empty space.

Additionally, the Screen is not in space and time. Space and time is in it.

Both the Screen and the Box are good working models for everyday experience. As I will explain in later chapters, the Screen is better in its application to the enigmas of modern physics, to things that happen at dimensional extremes. As we approach dimensional extremes, the Screen begins to fall apart. Ironically, it is the falling apart that enables us to see the Screen at all. We can see how it falls apart, and therefore, how it is put together. The structure of the Screen shows itself only at its outer limits, where it begins to unravel. Where we experience ordinary dimensions—in the "middle latitudes" of space, time, and mass—the Screen is virtually impossible to see because it is everywhere. It is like the fish with no concept of water: he has to jump out of the water to know that it is there.

What is the importance of a model like this? The Screen presents a scientifically rigorous picture of the essential oneness of spirit and world. It is the oneness of all things. Not a mere concept or belief, the Screen is a direct vision available both intellectually and experientially. If this model proves a useful way to understand human experience, it will have a profound effect on how we understand ourselves in relation to nature, and to each other.

A New Understanding of Ourselves

We need to reconsider who we think we are. Look at what we're facing in the world today! We are in a tenuous passage in our habitation of the earth. We don't know why we are affecting the climate. We don't know why we can't live peacefully with other tribes and other nations. We don't know why we are supposed to care for other forms of life. Before the current era, we did not have to care for anything other than human life. Now we do, and this is all new. We need to reinterpret our entire existence on the earth. We need a new concept of ourselves and of the purpose of our existence.

The model of the Screen and the new paradigm it presents is going to change us. I cannot say how it will change us, but I know that it will. Modern physics has shown us the limits of the dimensional world. It has also shown us that the world continues beyond the dimensions. We are not limited by space and time. Human consciousness transcends the dimensions and goes beyond anywhere we have previously considered. I find this heartening because the limitations we face are within the dimensions, within the physical portion of the spiritual world.

We are now on the verge of a spiritual revolution. The unity of consciousness is the unity of life, and the transcendent unity of life will bring humanity into harmony with the natural world. A new understanding of ourselves in relation to the world is exactly what is called for now. As a matter of survival, as an adaptation to new realities, we will have to grow spiritually, and as the quantum Screen model demonstrates, there is plenty of room to grow beyond the physical world.

— 1 —

The Quantum Screen

Let's begin with some general information about the quantum screen, and then I will detail the specifics of how it works.

Overview

In the last hundred years physicists have begun to look past the dimensional world into places where dimensions break down. They have discovered that when an object moves close to the speed of light, weird things begin to happen because velocities in that range strain the structure of the Screen. The Screen is based on the space-time structure of light. "c," the speed of light, is equal to 300,000,000 meters of space per second of time. In other words, a second is the same thing as c meters. This means that you can only fit 300,000,000 meters in a second. When you try to fit in more than c, you encounter serious distortions.

Physicists have also seen that space and time are not perfectly continuous the way we thought they were. Instead, the dimensional world, like a pixel screen, is grainy. Individual pixels on the screen are quanta, or little packets of energy. In the realm of vision, individual pixels are photons, or light quanta. Science is beginning to realize that the dimensional world is limited, that it exists within some larger context.

The quantum screen is a five-dimensional structure within which we experience the five sensory realms of sight, sound, taste, touch, and smell. As I will explain in more detail later in this chapter, space and time organize and coordinate what we see, hear, taste, smell, and touch.

As you feel your feet against the floor, and smell the bread in the oven and taste the coffee, as you look around the room and listen to the sound of footsteps in the hallway, the space and time that you experience are the dimensional structure of consciousness. This is the quantum screen, or perceptual consciousness as a whole.

This next part may be a little confusing, so pay close attention!

The quantum screen is only one aspect of a larger model of consciousness. I call the larger model the Screen, with a capital 'S.' It is a single reality with three separate but overlapping manifestations:

- the photon screen (visual consciousness)
- the quantum screen (perceptual consciousness)
- the observation screen (collective consciousness)

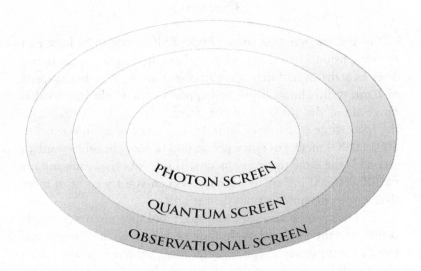

The quantum screen is an extrapolation of the photon screen, and the observation screen an extrapolation of the quantum screen. Each is experienced as a separate realm (or in the case of the quantum screen, as multiple realms) of consciousness; but each screen opens into the other two and constitutes, with them, a single entity: the Screen, with a capital "S".

You can think of each manifestation of the Screen telescoping out from the smaller one before it, that is, of the photon screen (what you see) expanding in all directions beyond vision to become the quantum screen (what you perceive in all sensory realms), and the quantum screen expanding in all directions to become the observation screen (what you hear about from others). Or, you can think of each larger manifestation contracting into the next smaller one, that is, of everything you know from observers concentrating into only what you can perceive yourself, and of everything you perceive concentrating into only what you see. A wider view opens as you look through one manifestation into the next, or a greater concentration of detail appears as you narrow back down. At each level the quality of experience is distinct, but structurally identical. The space-time-mass of each is the same, so that each passes seamlessly into the next. The three are one, and the one, three. For narrative simplicity, I will refer to each as a *screen*, rather than a *manifestation*, and of the three together as *the Screen*. I will describe each screen in turn, but the central focus of Part I of this book is the quantum screen—perceptual consciousness. The quantum screen is what each of us experiences directly as the physical world. This is the screen that we feel the body "in," or "on."

The quantum screen is quite literally the central concept of this book in that it lies between the other two. The observation screen is the larger world that observers as a whole experience, and photon screen is the smaller visual portion of perceptual experience as a whole. The Screen has no external existence—it is merely the space-time-mass structure within which physical reality is experienced. It is not in space and time; it *is* space and time. Space-time is in it.

The Screen is not reality, of course, but a model of reality. I mean by this that the physical world behaves very much like a three-dimensional pixel screen or a holograph, moving through time. Because physical objects behave on both the quantum and everyday level like patterns of points in five dimensions, a discontinuous pixel screen becomes a good representation of physical reality.

A quantum is a point in five dimensions—a tiny dot of energy, or an activated pixel of the screen. (Space-time is the order in which quanta—or pixels—are arranged to create the Screen.) A quantum is extremely small but not infinitely small. Because quanta are discrete points of energy, the quantum screen is not smooth or continuous, but grainy. Physical objects in space are like newspaper photographs, composed of many tiny points that together create an image. Physical objects are ranges of points on the Screen—points so small they cannot be seen, even with a powerful microscope. The mind connects the dots, creating the picture experienced as the perceptual consciousness of everyday living.

The Screen is better than the conventional view of physical reality because, as you will see, it does not require a material world beyond actual perceptual experience. It offers a better way to understand what science has been trying to tell us for over a hundred years.

The Screen is not the whole of consciousness. It is only the dimensional portion of consciousness. The Screen exists within a larger context that includes *non-dimensional* experience such as thought, emotion, dream, imagination, and spiritual experience. These are experienced outside of the dimensions and outside of the physical world. They are as real as tables and chairs, the only difference being that they are not in space, so they are non-dimensional. Non-dimensional experiences do not coordinate with dimensional experiences—you do not touch an object where you imagine it.

What makes the Screen unique is that, unlike non-dimensional consciousness, the five realms of perceptual experience are inter-coordinated. Each realm corresponds to a dimension, creating a single world from five separate forms of information.

Diving Into the Details

How does the Screen do this? Let's dive into the details.

The Screen has five dimensions: three of space (length, depth, height); one of time; and one of mass, which shows up on the Screen as a *second* time dimension (this will be explained later).

If the Screen is five-dimensional, and we have five realms of sensory perception (seeing, hearing, touching, tasting and smelling), the question arises: Is this mere coincidence? Might there be a direct, one-to-one correspondence between the dimensions and the sensory realms? How might the Screen coordinate the senses into a picture of physical reality?

Notice that where and when we see an object in space and time is also where and when we touch it, or hear it, or taste it, or smell it. The dimensions seem to coordinate perceptual experience into the picture we call physical reality.

Here's an example: You are sitting at a table with a vase of fragrant roses in front of you. What is your actual experience? What is visual? What, and where, is tactile perception when you reach out to touch what you see? What, and where, is the olfactory experience? Notice that these experiences are coordinated. The vase of roses seen "out there," can also be touched and smelled right at the spot where it is seen. You might say there is just a vase of roses on a table and you are seeing, touching, and smelling it. That is the way it seems on the surface. But this is not looking closely enough at how actual experiences in the realms of perception are interrelated to become a vase of roses.

Let's back up a little and talk about dimensions, as this will provide a more thorough understanding. The key to understanding dimensions is to realize that information is always an *actual* within a *potential*. Information is always something that *could be* something else. It is a yes that could be a no, a dot that could be a dash. It is a black pixel that could be a white, red, or purple pixel. Information is always a pattern that could be some other pattern. The potential, or the context, is what gives meaning to the actual. If I say *fifteen…*, the number by itself has no meaning. But if you know I'm talking about the number of dollars in your bank account, *fifteen* means you are likely to be hungry very soon. Or if I am talking about the number of runs the Red Sox scored in the third inning, *fifteen* means something very different. *Fifteen* is the same actual in two different potentials.

In the case of perceptual consciousness, we have five entirely distinct forms of information (seeing, hearing, touching, tasting and smelling), each with its own potential. The quantum screen creates dimensions out of those separate potentials and puts them together into space-time-mass. The result is a five-dimensional picture in which physical objects appear where and when they are *potentially* perceived in any other perceptual realm. Where and when you hear an object is also where and when you potentially see it. That's how the Screen works. This is analogous in some ways to an icon on a computer screen: if you see it at a particular location you can "click" on it and thereby taste or touch it at that same place. This coordination of sensory potentials on the Screen makes physical objects seem to exist independently of perceptual experience. It makes them appear to be material. They look as though they are sitting in space waiting for us to touch or to taste them.

Mass, the Fifth Dimension

Now let's return to the issue of mass showing up on the screen as a second time dimension—the fifth dimension in the Screen. The fifth dimension is an actual physical presence we experience everyday, more or less at "right angles" to space-time.

There are four dimensions of space and time:

- length
- height
- depth
- time

The fifth dimension, *mass*, is something we experience *foreshortened* in four dimensions. Let me explain: Your house has length, width and height; it is three-dimensional. But if you take a camera outside and snap a photo of your house, the photo will show the house on a two-dimensional surface. Even though the photograph is two-dimensional, you see the third dimension by a shortening of the other two. The third dimension does not exist in the *medium* through which you are looking at the house (the photo) but you can tell it is there. Through foreshortening, the picture looks like three-dimensional space, so you can have a three-dimensional experience through a two-dimensional medium.

Foreshortening in time is similar to that in space: a five-dimensional experience is possible in four dimensions of space and time. The fifth dimension is mass, which, as you may recall, shows up on the screen as a second time dimension. Mass corresponds to the tactile realm of perception, or the body. We feel mass when we push objects around or try to lift them in a gravitational field.

We feel mass in our muscles and on our skin when objects come in contact with our body. But where does this second time dimension come from?

The second time dimension has to do with acceleration, a form of motion that is distinct from simple velocity. I apologize for getting into physics here, but it is very important to stress the difference—*the big difference*—between velocity and acceleration. Velocity is measured in terms of space per time: miles per hour or meters per second. It has two dimensional components: one each of space and time. Acceleration is a *change* in velocity, and is measured in terms of meters per second *per second*. That's three dimensional components: one of space and two of time. There is also a huge difference in how we *experience* acceleration versus velocity. We *feel* acceleration, but we do not feel velocity. The first time dimension is not experienced in the body. For example, if you are sitting in an airplane moving at five or six hundred miles per hour, you do not feel anything you would not feel at zero or a million miles per hour. Looking out the window, you can see that you are moving, but you don't feel the movement in your body. What you *do* feel is *change* in velocity. On the runway, as the plane accelerates for takeoff, you feel your body being pushed back into the chair. When this happens, you are feeling the second time dimension. You also feel it with changes in the *direction* of velocity: right or left, up or down. You feel the vibration of the engines, bumps in the runway, and air turbulence. These changes in velocity, however slight, are actually accelerations. I identify the second time dimension with the tactile realm of consciousness because you feel it.

If we understand mass as a dimension, we do not have to understand it as a measure of material substance, that is, of something independent of conscious perception.

Einstein's Theory of General Relativity

Here is another mini-lesson in physics—this one on the topic of Einstein's Theory of General Relativity, or at least the part of it that is important to understanding mass as a dimension.

Einstein never said anything about a mass dimension, but a lot of what he did say points in this direction. He said that gravity, rather than being a force, is a curvature of four-dimensional space-time. An object at rest in the curvature of the earth's gravitational field, for instance, accelerates toward the earth. If you are standing on the surface of the earth, a falling object appears to be accelerating downward, hitting the floor (and possibly breaking); but it is really *you* that is accelerating *upward*. In the bottom of your feet you feel a tactile sensation of gravity that is identical to that of acceleration. The surface of the Earth is accelerating you up in the curved space-time of the Earth's mass. Falling objects are actually *at rest* in the curvature. In the Theory of General Relativity, Einstein called this the *Principle of Equivalence:* the equivalence of gravity and acceleration. I suggest that gravity and acceleration are the mass dimension at work. The curvature Einstein speaks of is a curvature into an additional dimension. This curvature is analogous to the curvature of the two-dimensional surface of the earth into a third dimension.

I will share more about Einstein's theories of General and Special Relativity in the chapter on physics and the quantum screen.

What Does this Dimensional Coordination Mean?

Simply stated, it means there is nothing "out there" beyond the images themselves. When we look away, there is nothing waiting in space for us to see or touch or taste. This is how the Screen differs from the Box, the conventional view in which space and time are fundamental structures of a universe that exists with or without consciousness. The Box understands consciousness to be inside the dimensions along with physical objects. On the Screen, we experience the physical world the same way as in the Box, but an imaginary material universe is not needed. Existence is limited to what we actually experience.

I just said we experience the physical world on the Screen the same way as we do in the Box. That might sound confusing, but here again, the difference is in where we are looking from, not in what we are looking at. The quantum screen model does not change the world; it changes us. With the quantum screen we are looking at the same physical world as with the Box, but from an entirely new perspective. That new perspective makes all the difference. With the quantum screen we no longer need material substance to do science or to do everyday life: with the quantum screen what you see is what you get.

There is no material world separate from actual experience. There is no duality. The belief that matter is "out there" produces the duality, but the duality is unnecessary.

Consciousness is Not "Self"

The Western tradition does not understand consciousness well. I do not mean that the East is metaphysically right and the West wrong; I mean that while the West has done a better job understanding how the physical world works, the East has done a better job understanding how the mind works. Sitting and looking at consciousness from the "inside" is a well-developed tradition in many Asian societies, but until recently, it was generally unpracticed in the West.

The most fundamental misconception in the Western tradition is the identity of consciousness with self. Consciousness and self are considered to be the same, but they are not. We will never understand what physics is trying to tell us so long as we think of consciousness as "us."

It's very important to understand that the Screen exists without the self. The self is not the same thing as consciousness; it is an element of consciousness—a focus of order through which conceptual consciousness interacts with perceptual. The self exists; but it exists as a curvature of experience, a focal point that distorts reality for its own purposes. The self is necessary for doing things (which we'll discuss in a later chapter). It distorts and reduces or magnifies what we see on the Screen, but it is not the Screen. There is no seer and no seen, only the seeing.

Many people understand that reality is ultimately unitary, or non-dualistic. But if you identify conscious experience as self, you

33

are trapped into thinking that the world *is* yourself. If consciousness is all there is, the world must be me. There is no absolute proof that anything or anybody exists other than me, so I must be the ultimate reality. In philosophical circles this concept is known as the solipsism.

The solipsism is a non-duality. It eliminates the divide between consciousness and the physical world. It is consummately logical and consistent with physical science, but also infantile and absurdly complicated and reductionist. In Copernican terms, the solipsism would be like suggesting that the Earth really is the center of the universe, that the sun revolves around the Earth, and that the rest of the universe revolves around the sun. While conceivable, such a proposition would require an entire new set of physical laws. To avoid the solipsism, we must learn to see the physical world beyond the curvature of self. Scientists are not trained to do this. Sensing the solipsism lurking in the curvature, they generally avoid non-dualistic thought.

— 2 —

A MEDITATION

In the next chapter I will go deeper into the physics of the quantum screen. But first I'd like to take you on a journey to actually *experience* the quantum screen.

Now that we're beginning to understand how the quantum screen works, we can go beyond the naive assumption that matter exists independently of experience. We do not all have to become Buddhists and Hindus but, by learning and practicing the mental disciplines within these traditions, we will develop new insights into a number of things we already know. Familiar phenomena will seem very different from a new point of view.

Meditation is looking, only looking. It is looking past thought, labels, categories, assumptions, words, and beliefs. It is looking at what is really there. The best way to keep your mind from wandering—from thinking about things while meditating—is to eliminate distractions by sitting still, usually with eyes closed. Make yourself comfortable so you do not have to move often. It's okay to move or to open your eyes if you need to, but if you keep this to a minimum, you will see further into what is there.

To practice meditation you don't have to have a belief system. You don't have to practice any religion. I will not be talking about Buddhism or Hinduism here, though one should recognize that meditation has developed over thousands of years through religious (primarily Eastern) traditions. We should honor those traditions. If one borrows a tool from a neighbor he should be respectful of the neighbor, and of the tool.

The irony here is that I will be asking you to look beyond labels, words, and concepts, yet these are all I have to offer as a guide.

The text of the meditation is written below, but I highly recommend you access the free download of this guided meditation at wetwaremedia.com/avery. By listening instead of reading you will be able to "see" directly.

The Quantum Screen Meditation

To begin, sit comfortably in an upright position with your feet on the floor and close your eyes. We'll begin to look at what is. Meditation is looking at the smallest and subtlest of things, so we'll look at experience in its most basic forms, and look past thinking as much as possible.

Let's start by looking at the various parts of your body from the inside. Begin with your feet. Feel them on the floor. Feel your ankles... and then your knees. Feel one knee and then the other, from the inside.

If you're sitting in a chair, bring your attention to the back of your legs on the chair. Your backside against the seat and your lower back against the back of the chair. Notice the tactile sensation in these parts of the body. Move your attention to your upper back and shoulders... your upper arms and elbows... focus on one elbow and then the other... and move your attention to your forearms... and your hands... Now look individually at each of your fingers. Perhaps they are touching each other. Feel your spine through your back, into your neck and up into your head. Feel your jaw... your teeth... and your eyes... Feel the hair on top of your head.

Now, looking past the categories and labels I've just mentioned, try to sense all the parts together simultaneously. Try to sense your whole body. Look beyond the words I have said; look from within to see what is there. Look at what you are feeling in parts of your body without thinking of the labels.

Anything you can name or put a label on... an arm... elbow... finger... these are gross sensations. But if your mind is very, very still you can see past the labels, past the arms, elbows and fingers.

Behind the gross sensations it is possible, with a very quiet mind, to experience billions of tiny points of energy throughout all parts of the body. These are subtle sensations.

These are the cells in your body... billions of them. These are quanta, tiny points of energy. They are very difficult to feel or to sense, but if you catch a glimpse of them you might wonder... are perceiving them... or imagining them? Is this "objective" experience or "subjective" experience? These subtle sensations, these tiny quanta, are beyond the duality of subject and object. These tiny quanta are on the edge between what we call subject and object. When you experience them, you are not you. There is no self and no world.

The larger gross sensations, the arms... legs... fingers... neck... elbows... are waves of quanta, or patterns of subtle sensations. They are collections of cellular sensation in the body. We experience these as objects in the physical world.

Now let us look at another type of experience in the body: the chemical realm of perception. Bring your attention to your mouth... throat... stomach... and throughout the digestive tract. This is the realm of perception we call taste. It is much more than taste. Tactile sensation is experienced on the exterior of a cell's membrane; chemical perception is experienced when chemicals pass through the membrane into the cell's interior. You are experiencing this chemical realm now. You experience it all the time as chemicals enter cells in parts of your body.

The tactile and the chemical realms are cellular experience. Right now, every cell in your body perceives on the surface of its membrane as well as within. As a multi-cellular being, you experience collections of cellular experience. Through these two realms—taste and touch—you keep an eye on your cells, and they keep an eye on you. The tactile and the chemical realms are essentially what you are: they are what you feel, and how you feel.

But cellular sensations are not physical objects. The gross sensations you feel on your skin and in your stomach become objects when you perceive them in the "higher" realms of seeing, hearing, and smelling. Without seeing, hearing, or smelling, an "object" is nothing more than a large multicellular sensation experienced in both the tactile and chemical realms at the same time. Time is the connection between the tactile and chemical realms. Space is the connection among all five sensory realms.

You may not be smelling much of anything right now. Humans are very limited in their ability to smell, but you are conscious in this realm. In the olfactory realm, you perceive objects at a distance from the body: in space. You do not have to touch something in order to smell it. Olfactory sensation is the experience of sensory cells in your nose... it is a chemical experience... but the experience is not the object you smell. The object is at a distance from the body. When you smell something you can also touch and taste it in the same location. Through space there is a potential for olfactory sensation to coordinate with tactile or chemical sensation.

Now... move your attention to any sounds around you... footsteps, birds, insects, traffic. Imagine the spatial world that comes along with these sounds. Each sound-producing object is in a direction from the body. This direction from your body is auditory space. Hearing is reducible to tactile sensation, but it is distinct from the tactile realm. This spatial world is beyond the experience of the cells themselves. This is the multi-cellular world.

With practice, very focused attention, and an extremely calm mind, you can eventually see through this world and directly feel the subtle sensations of individual cells... you can actually feel the quanta. This can take many years of intense practice, but there is an easier way to do this. There is a way to easily have a direct experience of individual cells. Let's look there now.

Bring your attention to the part of your body where you would be seeing things if your eyes were open. We're going to look at the field of vision... but without the vision. You may see flashes of light. You may see shadowy patterns of flickering light. If you look very closely and carefully you'll see individual points of what looks like light flashing on and off: tiny points of energy dancing around in an endless storm of "on and off." You are seeing the voices of individual cells in your retina. Are they really there, or are you imagining them? They are there. You are looking at the very limits of the physical world, the edge of the universe... You are looking at the quantum screen.

Notice, as you look at your retina with eyes closed, that it remains part of your body as a whole. Your field of vision is an oval-shape, more or less, surrounded by the rest of the tactile realm. You feel arms and legs and shoulders on all sides. You feel chemical sensations in your mouth and stomach. Beyond your body, in space, you sense the possibility of smell; and in directions from your body you hear objects in space. In the middle of it all, up close, is the visual portion of the quantum screen—the photon screen without the photons. You are still seeing the little dots of energy flashing on and off, and still feeling collection of cellular sensation in other realms. What is different about the retinal cells? How is it that you can perceive them individually when you cannot feel individual cells in your neck or toes? There is something special about the visual realm of consciousness. Let's look a little further...

Now, very slowly and carefully, open your eyes just the tiniest bit. Let in a little crack of light at the bottom of your field of vision. Light is the visual realm of consciousness. Notice the difference between the upper part of the field, which is still dark, and the lower part, where you are beginning to see objects differentiated in space. The little dots of energy flashing on and off are still everywhere, but they are lining up into clear patterns, becoming shapes in space. Where the light has come in, the dots have become dots of color. The patterns of dots are much more highly defined than gross sensations in the rest of the body. As patterns arise, the dots become less noticeable. The mind is drawn to the patterns. You are still experiencing quanta, but you no longer see them individually. The photon screen is melting into the physical world.

Each point of color is a quantum that has become a photon, or a particle of light. Arms and toes and shoulders are patterns of non-photon quanta. You are perceiving both photon and non-photon quanta. Like a single pixel on a television, the fundamental element of the Screen is the quantum, whether it's visual or non-visual. The fundamental structure of the Screen—the three-dimensional space you are beginning to see—comes from light.

As the quanta at the lower portion of your field of vision become actualized as photons, that portion of the quantum screen becomes the photon screen—the visual realm of perception.

The photon screen is the visual portion of the much larger quantum screen, the screen that coordinates vision with hearing, smelling, taste, and touch. Yet the quantum screen derives its three space dimensions from the photon screen—from light. The quantum screen is an extrapolation in all directions beyond the photon screen, beyond vision.

Now, open your eyes all the way... and watch shapes form in space. Looking around, you may feel your awareness "returning to the room," but you are still looking at the photon portion of the Screen. You no longer see the dots flashing on and off. The patterns of quanta hide the individual quanta. The world appears to be smooth and continuous.

But now, with eyes open, you are hearing and touching, perhaps smelling and tasting, as well as seeing. The quantum screen extends infinitely in all directions beyond the photon screen, becoming the universe. When you hear something behind your head or in another room—something you cannot see— you experience it in space, where you would see it if you were looking there. You hear it where and when you potentially see it. This is an example of the dimensional structure of consciousness, derived from light and applied to the auditory realm, and to every other realm as well.

As you walk through the day, everything you see and hear, everything you taste, smell, or touch, you experience within the dimensions of the quantum screen. This is the physical world.

— 3 —

PHYSICS & THE
QUANTUM SCREEN

Light is visual consciousness.

The structure of space-time is derived from light.

Physicists have spent the last several hundred years trying to find light inside of space and time. They have thought of dimensions as something "out there," and light as something bouncing around inside the dimensions, reflecting off objects and entering the eye. But light does not act like anything else in space-time. It is sometimes a wave and sometimes a particle, but never both at once. It has momentum (velocity times mass) but no mass, which, of course, is a mathematical absurdity. Light always travels at the same speed. It accelerates from 0 to 186,000 miles per second in 0 seconds. Light sets a speed limit for all objects in the universe, and travels at a constant speed *relative to all objects in the universe* (even if they are traveling at different speeds relative to each other). Physicists have never found a medium for light waves in space. They define space in terms of light (a line in space is the path of a light beam), yet they keep light *inside* the space it defines. This is like looking for a house inside a room of the house you are looking for.

In the discussion that follows, keep in mind that much of the quandary in modern physics is rooted in the belief that light is inside of space and time. Keep the Screen in mind. Again, pardon the physics, but try to follow as much as you can.

Einstein's Theory of Special Relativity

Let's talk about special relativity. This can be fun because we get to fly around in space ships and ride motorcycles at half the speed of light—at least in our imaginations. Much of special relativity is a "thought experiment"—trying out things that can only be thought about because they are too difficult to perform in real life. To be science, however, thought experiments must be consistent with experimental evidence gathered in other ways.

The story here goes back before the 20th century, into the late 1800's when physicists were trying to find a medium for the transmission of light. It was known that light consisted of waves, but what did the waves consist of? Ocean waves are waves of water and sound is waves of air, so light waves had to be waves *of something*. They had to be in a material medium of some sort. If that medium could be detected, not only would science know what light is, it would also be able to establish an absolute space throughout the universe. Every point in space would have a fixed position in the universe. Physicists were so sure that they would eventually find this medium that they gave it a name—the *ether*—and set about to find out what it was.

The 1890s were years of great optimism in physics. Physical science had already answered nearly all the great questions it had asked itself. Only a few missing pieces were needed to complete the picture of the physical universe. One of the missing pieces—perhaps the biggest one—was detection of the ether. The ether was thought to be an extremely subtle substance filling the entire universe. Because the Earth moved through space, it must move *in relation* to the ether. If the Earth's motion through the ether were detected, the discovery would establish an absolute reference point for space itself. The ether had to be everywhere... otherwise, how could light travel to Earth from the stars?

Scientists conducted a series of experiments to detect the Earth's motion through the ether, but every trial came out negative. Nobody could find what light was moving *in*. This was frustrating—disastrous even. There had to be ether or the world would no longer make sense. Then, in 1905, Albert Einstein (who was not a professional physicist at the time) came along and said that the reason ether had not been detected was that it does not exist. Light moves in waves, but not waves *of* anything. There is no medium—no substance doing the waving.

This was a mind blower! But the rest of what Einstein said about light was far worse. To make sense of what was now known, he had to introduce a whole new way of understanding physical reality.

Einstein observed that light moves at the same velocity *relative to everything*. How can that be? If things are moving about in the universe at different speeds relative to each other, how can one thing—light—move at the same speed relative to them all? Let's do a thought experiment here to illustrate what he said.

A Thought Experiment

Let's say that you and I are standing on a street corner and you have a gun that fires bullets at a thousand miles per hour. You and I each have a portable laboratory we carry around with us wherever we go, so we can measure anything. (Hey, this is a thought experiment, so we can do anything we like!) You fire the gun and we both measure the velocity of the bullet to be 1000 miles per hour.

Now, you hop on your motorcycle, spin around the block, and drive by me at 500 miles an hour. I'm still standing on the street corner. As you drive by, you fire the gun. You measure the velocity of the bullet to be a thousand miles per hour relative to you, as expected. I measure your velocity on the motorcycle to be 500 miles an hour. How fast am I going to measure the velocity of the bullet?

Easy: add 500 to 1000 and get 1500 miles per hour. When I actually measure the bullet's velocity, this is the number I get. Velocities add up. This is common sense.

But now, let's do something different. Put the gun away. This time you spin around the corner on your motorcycle and drive by me at half the speed of light. That's really fast! The speed of light, represented as '*c*' is 186,000 miles per second. Just as you pass me standing on the street corner, you turn on your headlamp. You will measure the velocity of the light coming out of the headlamp to

43

be *c*, the velocity of light. Obviously, right? But what about me? I measure your velocity to be one half *c*. How fast am I going to measure the velocity of the light coming out of your headlamp? Common sense would say it should be one and one half *c*. *But it's not. It's only c!* Light travels at the same velocity relative to me and to you, no matter how fast we may be moving relative to each other.

Light travels at the same velocity relative to everything. This is revolutionary. It changes everything. It means that there is something about light that is more fundamental than velocity, more fundamental than space and time.

Einstein also said that nothing can travel faster than the speed of light. You've probably heard that before. But if space is just emptiness, what is it about space that keeps physical objects from traveling faster than the finite value of *c*? Why can't they travel as fast as they want to?

Here's what happens when they try. Let's say you're back on your motorcycle driving by me at half the speed of light. As you whiz by me, I look into the physics laboratory you carry with you on your motorcycle, and I see some weird things going on in your *reference frame*. (That's your laboratory and the place from which you measure things. You are not moving in relation to your reference frame, and I'm not moving in relation to mine; but the two reference frames are moving in relation to each other.)

As I look into your reference frame I see some very unusual things happening. Space is shortening in the direction of your motion. Time is slowing down. And worst of all, mass is *increasing*. Every object in your laboratory has gotten heavier. We both have cell phones, so I call you to tell you about the strange things I see going on in your laboratory. You look around your laboratory—your reference frame—and notice that everything is normal: no shrunken space, no slowed time, no increased mass. Then (in the nanosecond you pass me), you look into *my* laboratory and tell me that space has shrunk, time slowed down, and mass increased in *my* reference frame. I check, but everything in my laboratory looks perfectly normal to me. We can't agree on what is happening, but we can measure the *dilations* (the shrinking, slowing, and increasing) and notice that they are proportional to each other and to our relative velocity. This means that, if we adjust for our relative velocity, we can know exactly what the dilations will be in each other's reference frame. But we still don't know why they exist.

That the dilations exist in the real world is proven beyond any doubt. The thought experiment we just did is based on a century of physical evidence. The dilations are very real. The only reason they are not noticed in everyday life is that people don't drive motorcycles that fast. The universe really is this weird at dimensional extremes. It is weird even at normal dimensions, but our relative velocities are so small that we do not notice anything unusual as we go about our everyday lives.

The dilations of special relativity are distortions of space, time, and mass. In other words, they are dilations of the Screen. They are proportional to the velocity of light. They have to do with what you're telling me about what you see, and with I tell you about what I see: in other words, they have to do with consciousness.

E = MC²

One more thing: Einstein's famous equation $E = mc2$ originates in special relativity. Energy is equal to mass times the speed of light squared. Light again. What does *light* have to do with the relation of energy to mass? And why *squared* (multiplied by itself)? What could that possibly mean? Light seems to be much more than the stuff that pours through your window in the morning. The space-time structure of light is the foundation of the entire universe.

In physics, there is something called the equivalence of mass and energy, which means mass is the same thing as energy, multiplied by four dimensions of space and time.

$$\text{meters } x \text{ meters } / \text{ seconds } x \text{ seconds}$$

As we will see later, this also means that the tactile experience of individual retinal cells becomes the consciousness of the organism as a whole in the context of four new dimensions: the Screen. It means the basic building blocks of matter are not material, but that *energy* is the fundamental substance of perceptual consciousness.

General Relativity

Now let's talk more about general relativity, or at least touch on it. Special relativity is special because it applies only to reference frames (motor cycles, laboratories, etc.) that are moving at a *constant* velocity relative to each other. General relativity applies to *accelerating* reference frames. (Remember the difference between velocity and acceleration?) The basis of the General Theory of Relativity is Einstein's realization that gravity and acceleration are the same—they are identical. They may not look identical, but they are.

Here's another thought experiment: if you were in an accelerating spaceship, you and everything in the spaceship would "fall" to the rear of the ship. The back wall would feel like the ground, and all the objects around you would be "pulled" toward it. You would walk around on the back wall of the spaceship the way you walk around on the floor of a building in a gravitational field. You wouldn't be able to tell the difference between acceleration and gravity. That's the basis of the General Theory of Relativity.

But general relativity goes on from there. Let's introduce acceleration into our earlier thought experiment on special relativity. Instead of a motorcycle, let's switch to a space ship—you have a lot further to go this time.

A Birthday Thought Experiment

You and I are twins, and today is our birthday. We're both twenty years old. To celebrate your birthday you decide to take a ride in your spaceship. I go down to the launch pad to wish you a good trip. We're having cake later, so I ask you not to be gone long. You blast off, accelerate, and whiz by me at half the speed of light. I'm still standing on the launch pad. By this time we both know all about special relativity: everything looks shorter, slower, and more massive to me in your reference frame, which looks fine to you, and everything looks shorter, slower, and more massive to you in my reference frame, which looks fine to me. No surprises.

But then you decide you're having too much fun and tell me you won't be back in time for cake. In fact, you have decided to take a trip around the nearest star, Alpha Centauri, which is more than four light-years away. You set a course for the star, curve around it, and then head back to the Earth. You are gone for twenty years to the day. You land back on Earth and step out of the spaceship. It's now our fortieth birthday, and I greet you with "Happy birthday!"

"We're forty years old," I mention. You look at me strangely and say, "No, actually, I'm only thirty-five."

You have been gone for 20 years, so I insist you are now forty; but then I look inside your spaceship. I check your calendars and clocks. What you are saying checks out: according to your instruments, only fifteen years have passed while you were traveling through space at half the speed of light, even though twenty years have passed here on earth. And I *look* five years older than you!

What happened? Why have I aged more than you have? What is the difference? When you were on your motorcycle, or even when you took a quick spin in your spaceship on the first day, we were able to agree that the reference frame was different for each of us, and that time slowed down for each of us from the other's point of view. There was no *preferred* reference frame—neither one of us was "right." But now things are different. One of us lived fifteen years while the other lived twenty years at the same "time." Why was I the one who aged more?

The difference is this: you went through the process of *accelerating* up to half of the speed of light and *stayed in that reference frame for a long time.* I never accelerated. That's the only difference.

From the standpoint of what I am trying to say here (Einstein did not say this), when you accelerated you entered into another dimension, the mass dimension, and took a bit of a shortcut through the time dimension. I moved through more-or-less "square" space-time over the years, while you cut through on a diagonal in space-time-mass.

Both special and general relativity show us that the quantum screen is not perfectly square and not perfectly rigid. It has flaws. Space is built from time, and the relation between space and time is based on the space-time structure of light, "c," which is not infinite. As you will recall, there are only 186,000 miles of space in a second of time, and no more. When you try to put more miles into a second by going close to the speed of light, you strain the structure of the Screen. Some of those extra miles end up in the mass dimension.

Another way to understand the space-time structure of light is to realize that as you look out into space, whether you are looking across the galaxy or across the room, you are looking back in time. If you look at Alpha Centauri four light years in the distance, you are looking four years back in time. What you see is the star as it was four years ago. Even as you look across the room you're looking back a billionth of a second into the past.

On the quantum screen, space and time are the same thing. At extreme velocities, where space gets mixed back into time (miles per hour), the Screen becomes distorted, bending space dimensions into time and mass.

Quantum Mechanics

Quantum mechanics is the other branch of modern physics that has provoked a new understanding of the structure of consciousness.

The quantum was discovered a few years before special relativity. Max Plank ran across the first quanta in the year 1900. He found that energy, rather than being a perfectly smooth and continuous substance, was chopped up into little unbreakable bundles that he called *quanta*. A quantum is the smallest possible unit of energy.

Energy has five dimensional components:

$$\text{mass } x \text{ space } x \text{ space } / \text{ time } x \text{ time}$$

I consider the quantum a point in five dimensions. That's where we get the five dimensions of the quantum screen.

What Plank discovered was that even though physical reality looks perfectly smooth in everyday life, it is actually grainy. It's broken up into little points. One way to understand this is to think of a baseball flying over center field. When you look at the path of the ball, it appears to be a perfectly smooth arc across the sky. But if you were able to magnify what you were seeing several billion times, you would see that the baseball is actually moving in a bumpy, discontinuous manner from one set of quanta to the next, like an object moving across a very grainy computer screen, jumping from one set of pixels to another. Physical objects actually leap "across" the non-space between one set of quanta and another. Hence the term *quantum leap*. Physical reality is grainy. In everyday life we do not see the graininess, but it is there.

Think of a physical object much, much smaller than a baseball: an electron, for example, which is comparable in "size" to an individual quantum. If you track the path of the electron through space, rather than seeing a smooth arc, what you see is a series of points. The points are the only thing that is known about the location of the electron. You can say the electron was at this particular point in space at a particular time, and then moved to another point, and then another; and you can draw a line through all the points and call it the "path" the electron took, but in fact you know nothing—you *can* know nothing—about the location of the electron *between* the points. There really is no path, only the points. You cannot say the electron existed between the points. You cannot even say it was *the same* electron at more than one point. The mind draws the line between the points, but physical reality itself remains grainy. There is no space and no time between the points, and nothing, therefore, to "pass through." All we know is an electron was at this point at time one, and an electron at another point at time two.

The Uncertainty Principle

A physicist by the name of Werner Heisenberg expressed this phenomenon in a different way. He said that for an extremely small particle like an electron, it is *impossible to know* where it is if you know too much about its momentum (that is, how the electron is moving). The more you know about momentum, the less you can possibly know about location; and the more you know about location, the less you can possibly know about momentum. This is not due to the inaccuracy of our measuring instruments; this is a limitation built into the structure of the universe. It is known as the *Heisenberg Uncertainty Principle.*

There are limits to space and time, limits to how far we can extend the use of dimensions. The lower limit to the dimensional world is the quantum level (near the size of individual quanta). Anything smaller is no longer exactly *in* space. The upper limit is the speed of light. Beyond these limits space and time disintegrate into non-dimensional consciousness. Looking at subatomic particles below the quantum level is looking at the actual without the potential, looking at a "thing" without a distinct space-time context.

The Wave Function

Quantum phenomena are also expressed in terms of a *wave function*. You cannot know exactly where an electron is at a particular point in time, but you can know it is more likely to be in some places than in others. There is a distinct probability the electron will be here, and there is some other probability it will be there. The line connecting the points cannot determine exactly where the electron is, but it can be extrapolated to indicate where the electron is most likely to be. There is a greater probability the electron will be somewhere close to where the line is pointing than somewhere far from where the line is pointing. This probability can be expressed mathematically through the wave function.

Another realization that has accompanied the development of quantum physics is that we really cannot talk about an electron out there in space unless someone is looking at it. The *act of observation* has to be part of the overall understanding.

Quantum mechanics is extremely well established in the physical sciences. Its methods of describing particle behavior have been proven many times over, yet no one is quite sure what it all means. The problem, I believe, is in trying to understand consciousness in the Box with other physical phenomena. If, instead, the Box is put inside consciousness, and the concept of material substance is abandoned, quantum behavior becomes understandable.

All of the enigmas of modern physics have to do with light; all have to do with dimensional extremes; and all have to do with observation, or consciousness.

In everyday life we do not see the weird things that happen at dimensional extremes, but through science, we know they are there. Because we know they are there, we need a new model of perceptual consciousness that brings the enigmas and everyday life into a single understanding. The dimensions that disappear between quanta or stretch themselves out into black holes may seem light-years away from the front door, but they are the very same dimensions we walk through from the living room to the kitchen.

Inertial Mass

Before moving on to the next topic, there is one more very important physical phenomenon to mention, something physics has known about for centuries, but that does not fit in the Box. Not quantum mechanics or relativity theory this time—nothing at a dimensional extreme—something everyone experiences every day, every minute of every day: *inertial mass*. There is no generally accepted explanation in physics, modern or otherwise, for how inertial mass works. To get an object moving, it has to be pushed. Friction, of course, must be overcome, but I am not talking about friction. Even if you were in interstellar space with no gravity and no friction, you would still need to push things to get them moving. The more massive they are, the harder you need to push. Common sense says mass is a measure of matter, and it is the material substance within the object that resists acceleration. But how does that happen? How does matter "hold on" to space? And why does it hold on under *acceleration*, but not under constant velocity? Extremely massive objects like moons and planets move through space all the time with no resistance at all. How does matter "know" that it is accelerating? The Box has no explanation for this. One reason I feel justified in introducing mass as a dimension is that it explains inertial mass not within space-time, but as behavior within a dimension additional to space-time.

The curvature of the Earth expanded the medieval mind because it added a new dimension to the world. But the Earth still looks flat on the everyday level. Even today, so long as you do not travel too far, you can get away with thinking of the Earth extending endlessly without curving.

Like a flat Earth, the Box still works well on the everyday level—you can use it if you do not know too much. Eventually though, if you live in the larger world science has discovered, you will need the Screen.

— 4 —

THE EVOLUTION OF CONSCIOUSNESS

Consciousness evolves from the cell to the organism to the organization. Each higher level becomes a universe unavailable to the lower, yet exists only by virtue of the lower.

Within the Box, consciousness is commonly understood to be a complexity of mechanical interrelations emerging from unconscious matter. From the standpoint of the quantum screen, consciousness did not evolve within space or within time. Time evolved within it, as an essential structure of the Screen. We may still speak of the evolution of consciousness so long as we mean only its apparent manifestations within space and time.

The quantum screen need not be envisioned. It is not an abstraction. It is right here before you. Objects you see, hear, and taste are on the Screen. The Screen itself, as opposed to objects on the Screen, is difficult to experience directly. But as we saw in the meditation exercise, it can be experienced directly through the visual realm when there is no actual visual input. Eyes closed, one can "see" thousands of individual quanta in the field of vision. This ability to experience individual quanta is unique to visual consciousness. With eyes open, each photon is so small that what you actually see are *patterns* of photons. The screen is so fine-grained you do not notice it is there. The reason it is fine-grained is that in each retina there are about a million cells, each with a direct neural connection to the optic lobe of the brain. There are enough pixels, therefore, for objects on the screen to appear perfectly smooth and continuous in everyday life. What you *see* as light is what a million individual cells *feel* as points of tactile consciousness. Light comes in the form of waves or of particles. You see waves; individual cells feel particles. This is the *dual nature* of light.

How has the quantum screen evolved?

A living cell is an enclosure of organic molecules, a membrane separating the organized life process within from the chaos of the exterior environment. Beneficial chemicals are allowed through the membrane to become part of the metabolic process, while harmful chemicals are kept out. To live, therefore, a cell must distinguish one from the other. It must be able to distinguish beneficial from harmful chemicals and distinguish exterior from interior. The cell learns to "touch" objects in the environment before it "tastes" them (that is, before it lets them through the membrane). The cell senses pressure from the outside to know what to ingest and what not to ingest, so the structure of cellular consciousness evolves to include both the chemical and tactile realms of perceptual consciousness— what we call taste and touch.

As single cells combine into multi-cellular communities, or organisms, they retain this fundamental chemo-tactile structure of perceptual consciousness. The plant kingdom consists of multi-cellular communities that have not evolved beyond this structure. Though multi-cellular, perceptual consciousness in the case of plants remains limited to only the chemo-tactile realms. Cell communities that evolved into the animal kingdom, however, evolved specialized sensory organs and new realms of perception to go with them. The chemo-tactile realms remained the experience of each cell—of each cell even within the sensory organs—but the animal *as a whole* came to experience three "higher" realms of perceptual consciousness: the olfactory, auditory, and visual. An animal smells, hears, and sees, while its individual cells do not.

Individual cells, whether plant, animal, or unicellular, are only able to taste and touch. But these simple forms of cellular perception become building blocks of "higher realms" of perception. Everything *you* experience as a multi-cellular organism is experienced in some manner by the cells in your body. What you smell is the chemical experience of the olfactory cells of your nose; what you hear is the tactile experience of the cochlear cells of your ears; and what you see is the subtle tactile experience of the retinal cells of your eyes. Chemo-tactile experience becomes the raw material of smelling, hearing, and seeing.

To become meaningful , sensory information is experienced as an actual within a potential. The potential for each higher sensory realm is a dimension of space. Space is the context that relates information in any one realm to that in every other realm. Actual information within each higher realm is coordinated with every other realm through a single multi-dimensional potential. The quantum screen evolves from the unification of five entirely distinct forms of sensory information into a single five-dimensional picture of physical reality.

Smell

Smell, for example, is the chemical experience of specialized olfactory cells. Olfactory information is, therefore, *reducible* to the experience of individual cells in contact with airborne or waterborne chemicals. But smell is more than this. Olfactory consciousness is the experience of the organism as a whole, of an object at a distance from the body. This is where space comes in.

Olfactory cells "taste" chemicals through their membranes as the organism as a whole *smells* an object in space. The organism senses something "out there," in space, beyond where it touches or tastes. But through smell alone the organism cannot know exactly where in space the object is. The spatial structure of the olfactory realm is quite limited. To find the object without hearing or seeing it, the organism moves back and forth until it detects a chemical gradient, or a direction of increasingly stronger olfactory sensations. Through time-separated olfactory perceptions it *constructs* an additional space dimension from time. By sniffing here now, and then there, it senses a *direction* in which it can move to encounter the object, or to avoid it.

With the sense of direction constructed from time-separated olfactory sensation, the organism still has no idea how *distant* the object may be. If the organism senses increasingly strong sensations it will eventually be able to touch, or "find," the object. Animals with sensitive olfactory organs can "sniff out" space dimensions in this manner, though they never experience additional space dimensions in the olfactory realm alone.

Sound

In the auditory realm, a second space dimension, *direction,* is built into the information potential. Sound is experienced in the form of longitudinal waves of air or water. Cells in the cochlea (the hearing organ in the ear) experience time-separated tactile sensations that the organism hears as an auditory object at a distinct direction in space. The wave consists of tactile sensations repeated in time. Through time, the organism locates the direction of the auditory object: a sound wave arriving at an angle contacts one ear drum before another, or one part of a single ear drum before another. Through the time difference, the organism can determine direction. Again, space is constructed from time.

You can tell direction, but you cannot tell distance from hearing alone. If you happen to know what the object is, you may be able tell how far away it is; but if not, the sound could be from a quiet object up close or a loud object at a distance. There is no way to know. If you hear an unidentified sound, you know which direction to go to encounter or avoid it, but you cannot know how far to go in that direction. Unless, of course, you also *see* the object.

Sight

Light comes in the form of *transverse* waves. These are waves that are at right angles to the line of propagation, that is, perpendicular to the path the light is following. This means that there is an additional dimension embedded in the structure of light. The relative distances of objects seen in the same direction can be determined through superposition. Closer objects overlap more distant ones. If you move in the direction of two objects that you see, you will touch the superimposed object first. That is, the one closer to you. There is, then, a third space dimension built into the structure of light.

Coordinating a Five-Dimensional Picture of Physical Reality

Without the quantum screen there would be five separate one-dimensional worlds. There would be no organization of cellular into multi-cellular experience. The quantum screen coordinates five separate sensory potentials into a single five-dimensional picture of physical reality. It takes the structure of one realm, light, and imposes it on the other four. That is how the structure of light becomes the structure of the entire universe.

The mind, then, did not dream up space-time. It adapted space-time from actual experience—the experience of light—and applied it generally to sound, taste, smell, and touch. That is why objects are perceived in space where they *would be seen*. You may never look, but if you hear something in the next room or feel something behind your back, you will see it there if you do look. This is *potential* perception. Any object perceived in any perceptual realm is potentially perceived in all of them—at the same location in time and space. This potential perception makes the object seem material. To create a context for potential perception in the non-visual realms, the mind extends the space-time structure of light (the photon screen) in all directions beyond the field of vision to become the quantum screen. This is multi-cellular consciousness.

Space dimensions come only with the evolution of multi-cellular consciousness. Because the Box sees consciousness only within space and time—within an organism—it does not know what to do with multi-cellular consciousness. If consciousness is in the Box, where exactly in the Box is it? In one particular cell? In a group of cells? Somewhere in between cells? Or in all the cells? The Box tries to understand consciousness from the outside, as if it were something "out there," when there is no out there.

The Observational Realm of Consciousness

The evolution of consciousness does not end with multi-cellular organisms. Millions of years ago cells evolved into plants and animals, but now organisms themselves, especially humans, are evolving into *organizations*. Human societies are developing new collective structures of consciousness. A relatively new realm of consciousness, the *observational* realm, began to evolve many thousands of years ago and has now begun to dominate the perceptual realms. The observational realm has developed a dimensional potential and structural relation to the perceptual realms.

Observational consciousness is information from observers—what you hear about the world from other people. It extends much further than direct perception (personal experience) but remains *reducible* to perception; that is, observational *information* is seen or heard within the perceptual realms. (I *see* the newspaper; I *hear* you talking.) But observational consciousness is much more than perception. It presents physically real objects beyond the limits of an individual human's seeing or hearing, and thus beyond the quantum screen. Much of what we know about the world is observational, and beyond direct perception. We hear or see what is happening in other countries, other towns, next door, or the next room though the eyes and ears of observers. We do not have to be there to know what is happening.

We do not directly see what observers see. Information from them is coordinated with the perceptual realms the way the perceptual realms are coordinated with each other. If you look where and when I say I see an object in space and time, you will see it there too. You may also hear or touch it there.

The dimensional coordination of the information comes from *order* built into the sounds coming from my mouth. Something about how the sounds are put together creates the possibility that you can see for yourself what I am talking about. If I tell you I see a cat walking across my backyard, you know through my words that you could look there and see the cat. Usually you do not bother. Usually you take my word for it. But the fact that if you actually look you will see the object I am talking about makes observation another form of *potential perception*. If you look and the cat is not there, it is not potential perception and not observational consciousness. I am lying, or just mistaken.

The observational realm began to evolve with the development of symbolic language deep in the human past. When people were able to create sounds or signs that symbolized physical objects *where and when* they saw the objects, the observational realm was on its way. This was not "grunt and point." A degree of collective awareness arrived when one person made a sound and pointed at something he was seeing in the distance. But true observational consciousness begins only with symbolic expressions of space and time relations. Grunt and point means "I see something, now you look and see it for yourself," whereas observation means "You would see this thing I am talking (or writing) about *if* you were to look where I am looking... but you don't have to look because I'm telling you it's there." The difference is you don't have to look— I'm telling you what you would see. With or without perceptual backup, observational information creates a picture in the mind through the use of symbolic language. This is much more than calling attention to what one sees.

But how does observation appear on the Screen? The information itself comes through the auditory or visual realms: you hear sounds coming out of my mouth or you see words on the page. But the picture the information creates is not perceptual. You cannot see it or touch it. It's not on the quantum screen. It comes in a context closely related to the quantum screen, but it is not composed of quanta. It is imaginary, but because it is *potential perception*, it is a very special form of imagination. I call it the *observation screen*. It has the same dimensional structure as the quantum screen, but is one dimension larger. When I tell you about the cat walking across my yard, you imagine it there exactly where (and when) I describe it. The cat is on the Screen. You know it is there even though you cannot see it from where you are. But you *could* see (or touch or hear) the cat—that is what distinguishes the observation screen from ordinary imagination.

Observation appears on the observation screen, but also appears *foreshortened* on the quantum screen in the form of order. Six dimensions are reduced to five. Observers, like ordinary inanimate objects, move in five dimensions; but unlike inanimate objects, they also move in an orderly manner—an additional dimension. You can tell observers are alive by the way they move. They can change the rate or direction of their acceleration. Through the five-dimensional quantum screen, you can have a six-dimensional experience: you can see a living being run through the forest or walk down the street.

But there is a problem here: observation looks and sounds like imagination. I can tell you there is a cat walking across my yard when there is no cat. Whether there is or isn't a cat, my words sound the same to you. I could be lying, or I could be mistakenly telling you about a cat I think is there. Either way, there is no observational consciousness because there is no potential perception; you would not see a cat if you were to look for yourself. So every time I tell you about the cat, you are left wondering whether or not it is actually there. This is a great weakness in observational consciousness, an intolerable weakness. Observation has become so important to building the larger picture of the world that society has set up special safeguards against mistakes and against lying. If an observer claims a particular object or event is observational, we want to be sure it is potentially perceivable by other observers. We have evolved systematic means of testing what we think we see. It is called science. The scientific method tests observational statements to be sure they are perceivable by any other observer under the same conditions.

Science is the systematic growth of the observational realm of consciousness. This relatively new realm, beginning with language several thousand years ago, is now burgeoning in the scientific age. Science is an expanding universe of human consciousness infinitely larger than direct perception.

Several generations ago the world was primarily perceptual. People lived with the space and time they saw and heard in their own homes and neighborhoods. Now, through television, radio, computers, telephones, newspapers, and books, we experience a far larger world than can be perceived through our immediate senses. Computer and television images are nearly as clear and distinct as the quantum screen itself. We stare at pixel screens that penetrate directly into collective consciousness.

Increasing cultural and economic interdependence is accompanied by increasing interconnection of conscious experience. People around the world watch the same shows and see the same pictures on the Internet. Humanity is in an extremely rapid stage of collectivized evolutionary development. For hundreds of thousands of years we lived as any other organism in relation to its environment, each of us reacting individually to the world as we experienced it. Now we are an organizational system struggling to adapt to our own power in relation to the non-human world. Our continued existence depends on a continued expansion of awareness of ourselves in relation to each other and to the forests and fields, the weather, the oceans, and to the Earth as a whole. As individuals we were too small a part of life to be aware of its wholeness, but suddenly—very suddenly—we are interconnected. We have become a form of life that has never been before.

The evolution of higher levels of consciousness among humans parallels, in many ways, the evolution of higher levels of consciousness among individual cells as they developed into multi-cellular organisms.

— 5 —

SELF AND DOING

The quantum screen as I have discussed it to this point may seem entirely passive, as if one merely sits and watches the world go by on the Screen. If this were true, the quantum screen would not be a good model of physical reality, because one interacts with physical reality. We change things we see, move things around, and think of new arrangements in space and time. Then we bring arranged thoughts into physical reality: we *do* things. To be a complete model, the quantum screen has to show how conceptual consciousness (thinking) becomes perceptual: how what we think becomes what we see in the dimensions.

We interact with objects on the Screen. This is where the *self* comes in. The self is not consciousness; the self *does* things. The self interacts with the physical world through what I call *dimensional interchange*. Before I can explain how self is related to consciousness and how self creates *doing*, I must explain what I mean by dimensional interchange.

Dimensional Interchange

Why does consciousness *seem* to be in space? One reason is that we appear to move *through* space. From the standpoint of the quantum screen, apparent motion in space is explained by the interchange of one dimension for another. (*Doing* is a more complicated form of dimensional interchange—I will get back to it soon.)

The quantum screen has five dimensions of space, time, and mass, each corresponding to one of the five realms of perceptual consciousness. The visual, auditory, and olfactory realms correspond to space dimensions, and the taste and touch (chemo-tactile) realms to time dimensions. But the quantum screen is not static, it doesn't stay in one place: we move around. Consciousness itself does not move, but the dimensional framework of consciousness—the Screen—does appear to move. With the interchange of space for space, space for time, or mass for time or space, the body appears to move through space. With the interchange of mass for *order*, the self *does* things.

Right now, look east. Now look north. You have just made a space-for-space interchange. You can do this without moving your body, without even moving your head. You can do it by simply moving your eyes. What you see is a ninety-degree rotation of the entire universe. The commonsense understanding is of moving your eyes ninety degrees to the left but, because we know that space is relative, an equally reasonable understanding would be space as a whole shifting ninety degrees to the right. (Notice that we are not shifting *objects* in space, only space itself.) Both explanations work, and there is no real physical preference for one or the other. This is an example of a simple space for space interchange, which could be interpreted either as turning one's head ninety degrees in space or as space as a whole shifting ninety degrees.

A somewhat more complicated interchange is space for time, which appears as uniform velocity through space. If you're moving down the hall seeing doors and windows and pictures on the wall, everything is moving past you in the opposite direction. You can interpret this either as moving yourself through space or as "scrolling" space through the quantum screen. Either consciousness is moving north through space, or space is moving south through consciousness. The rate of the apparent velocity is the rate of interchange between one space dimension (the direction of motion) and time. As a dimensional interchange, this is a rotation of the axis of the time dimension into one space dimension. The greater the rotation, the more space moves by per unit of time, and the faster you appear to be moving.

A more complicated interchange is the rotation of the mass dimension into space or time. This rotation is experienced as uniform *acceleration* through space. As you accelerate down the hallway, all the doors and windows and pictures on the wall are moving by you at a faster and faster pace. As this is happening, you feel a tactile (or kinesthetic) sensation throughout your entire body. This feeling is the mass dimension as a whole, which corresponds to the tactile realm and identifies the tactile realm with the second time dimension of acceleration. Acceleration is measured in meters per second *per second*; the second "per second" is what you feel in your body. The greater the acceleration, the more you feel it. This is a linear acceleration.

You also experience *angular* acceleration: a curve in the path of your motion. This is another type of a change in velocity. (Velocity consists of both speed and direction: change in either is acceleration. Angular acceleration is a change in direction.) As you go around a curve you feel it in your body the same way you feel a linear acceleration. You are still moving at the same speed, but into another space dimension.

When you travel about, whether walking or riding, you feel things throughout your body. You feel your footstep against the ground or you feel the vibration of the wheels; you feel the starting up and the slowing down; you feel the going around corners and over bumps. These are all accelerations. If, in an ideal situation, you were to move perfectly straight forward on a perfectly smooth highway without any turns and without changing speed, you would not feel any acceleration at all. But in the real world you feel acceleration because you are constantly interchanging the mass dimension with time or space.

The Practical Realm of Consciousness

Doing is another form of dimensional interchange. To describe doing I must first introduce another realm of consciousness: the *practical* realm. This is a *conceptual,* not a perceptual realm of consciousness. Its dimension is *order,* the same dimension as observation. Like observation, the practical realm is a form of imagination; but unlike observation, it is not potential perception. The order you or I think of before we do something cannot be perceived or observed. Yet the practical realm is not ordinary imagination—it is not thinking of just anything—it is a specially structured realm of imagination coordinated with the perceptual and observational realms, a realm within which we imagine doing things *that can be done*. The practical realm of consciousness is imagination that can be successfully rotated onto the Screen.

Normally, you can tell an experience is perceptual rather than conceptually whether or not it can be verified in another realm. If you see something and you are not sure whether it is real or imaginary, you can listen for it or touch it to verify its physical existence. If the object or event is imaginary, you will not experience it in any other realm. If you imagine there is a lobster hanging on the wall, you may "see" it there, but if you reach over and do not feel it there, you know the lobster is imaginary. You know it's not real. Objects you "see" in the practical realm of consciousness are like this. They are imaginary; you cannot touch them. Yet what distinguishes the practical realm from ordinary imagination is that, under the right conditions, *you can bring the practical into the perceptual realms*.

While it is conceptual you cannot see and touch it, but if and when it rotates into the dimensions you *can* see and touch it. In doing things you create order in space-time-mass, order you were only thinking of before: you do what you were thinking of doing. But you can do what you are thinking only if it is physically possible.

Let's say you are standing in the living room and you are tired of looking at the furniture the way it is arranged. The sofa is by the door and the chair is next to the window, and you've had enough. You want to change how the living room looks. So you consider another arrangement: you imagine the sofa by the window and the chair near the table. This arrangement is accomplished in the practical realm of consciousness. It is a mental and not yet a physical experience. The order differs from the arrangement you see and touch, but you have actually experienced the furniture in the new arrangement in your mind. How can you bring this imaginary order into the physical world so that you can see and touch it?

You have to get your body behind it. You have to interchange order with mass. As you push the sofa to its new location, you feel the body rotate practical thought into physical reality. You feel the body—the whole body, or just a finger or tongue—whenever you rotate the practical realm into the world. Order interchangeswith mass.

If the order you imagine is truly doable, you will come to see and touch the sofa by the window and the chair by the table. This defines the practical realm of consciousness: to be doable it has to rotate into space-time. It has to be physically possible. If you imagine the sofa on the ceiling and the chair floating through space somewhere, you will not be able to do it. It's not going to work. Your imaginary experience is not within the practical realm.

Once you use your body to move things to a new location, you can touch them where you only imagined them before. You can see them there—they are on the quantum screen. Order moves from imaginary to actual quanta. This is doing. Doing is how we interact with what we see and touch and feel in the world around us.

It is the *self* that narrows consciousness to the concentrated order of doing. The self reduces the higher dimensional order of the physically possible to the physically actual—to observational consciousness. It ignores most of the full scope of imagination to concentrate on a single possibility. The wave function of imagination collapses into the dimensions. Self is a focus of order that connects with the body—legs, hands, fingers, or tongue—to do things. Self conceives new order and becomes the pivot point between practical thought and the body.

By doing, the self collapses consciousness to a smaller picture. It distorts the big picture into something it can manipulate. There is less room for detail, for insight, and for new possibility. For this reason, one tries to *do* as little as possible when practicing meditation. Doing limits the expansion of consciousness into the body, into the mind, and into the physical universe. Doing divides the universe into subject and object. When self is detached from consciousness, however, doing slips into the non-duality. The self appears against the background of non-self.

Looking looks past the self, turns, and looks back.

Order is conceived within the practical realm of consciousness. Unlike space, time, and mass, it is not quantifiable. Order is not as dimensional as the other dimensions because you can't put a number on it. It is difficult to say exactly what order is, but you know it when you see it.

All living beings bring order into the dimensions when they do things. The creation of order could, in fact, serve as a physical definition of life. Living beings do things; they create six-dimensional order from five-dimensional parts. You can see order in the way they move fingers, paws, legs, tails, tongues, and whole bodies. They move not only in a constant velocity, or even constant acceleration—they move in non-constant acceleration. They move as if they are alive. Living beings of all kinds move within the *potential* for observational consciousness. Only humans (for the most part) create *actual* observational consciousness for other humans. Humans create order in language, writing, architecture, music, sculpture, and cooking.

As you look around the room you see patterns that are distinctly orderly. The walls of the room are orderly. You know that a self, a human self, created the order. Somebody did it. There was a person—usually a person—who conceived the order you see and brought it into the physical world.

— 6 —

COLLECTIVE CONSCIOUSNESS

The quantum screen model is simpler than the Box because it does not require you to believe anything you do not see. You do not have to believe in a universe of material substance you can never experience directly. You feel, see, touch, hear, and taste things in space and time, but you do not experience anything beyond experience. You do not experience "matter." Your acceptance of the existence of material substance is an act of faith. You may believe in the existence of matter if you wish; but when you believe in it, you create the dualism of self and world. With the Screen you do not have to believe in matter in order to make sense of the physical world. You do not need the dualism to understand what you see.

A principle of meditation is to look at what is there, not at what we think might be there. The same principle applies to collective consciousness. We will not assume what we cannot see; we will look at what is there.

Right now I'm looking out the window. Across the street is a house on the corner. A car is parked to the left of the house and a tree stands on my side of the street. The sun is out and the sky is blue. The day is beautiful.

I have just created a picture in your mind, a picture that is not visual. You don't see what I'm seeing; yet you have an experience similar to my own. You "see through my eyes." But what you see is not on the quantum screen. Your actual experience is limited to a perceptual realm (seeing or hearing), but the only thing you actually perceive is letters on the page or the sound of my voice. As you read my words or hear my voice, you also experience a whole new realm of consciousness—collective consciousness (the observational realm). Collective consciousness remains *reducible* to perception—you simultaneously experience life collectively and individually.

Individual cells create organic consciousness much the way organisms create collective consciousness. Each cell experiences the chemical and tactile realms. Cells in the retina experience the tactile impact of photons. The mind assembles these into the dimensional picture of visual consciousness. My words describing the street outside my window are sounds you hear—sounds like raindrops pattering, dogs barking, or wind blowing in the trees. But my words do more than these sounds; my words evoke a higher dimensional arrangement of the auditory information you are receiving: they create a picture you "see" in your mind's eye. Your mind is tapping into a new level of consciousness over and above auditory perception. Anyone else listening (who understands English) would "see" a similar picture.

This is the observational realm of consciousness. It is not on the quantum screen; it is on the observation screen—a picture not of light, but of dimensionally structured imagination, based on the dimensional structure of light. That is why you "see" the picture in your mind's eye. The observation screen is not as clear and defined as the quantum screen; but because it allows for an infinitude of additional possibilities, it is a dimension larger than the quantum screen.

One often thinks of "collective consciousness" as the sum total of individual consciousnesses. This simplistic understanding is founded on unconscious assumptions. The larger dynamic of collective consciousness requires a re-examination of fundamental assumptions concerning the relationship between conscious experience and the physical world.

Collective awareness is not just an academic question. It is not just a matter of curiosity. Collective consciousness is a matter of who we are and who we are rapidly becoming. We are not what we were only a generation or two ago. One could safely say that a few decades ago people understood the world as they directly experienced it through perceptual consciousness. The world they lived in was the world they saw, heard, and felt personally. Now, most of what average people understand of the world comes through a medium of some form. We see through the eyes of other people. We hear through the ears of other people. We, as collectivized human beings, are an entirely new form of life on earth: a living presence that did not exist a few years ago.

Through electronic media we are evolving extremely rapidly. Computers, radios, televisions, telephones, satellites, and the Internet do not just make life easier; they create new forms of collective consciousness. They do not just help us do things; they change the way we experience life. We think of electronic gadgetry as lifeless mechanisms external to ourselves, but they are much more. They are organic expressions of the ongoing evolution of human consciousness.

Computers and pocket calculators are not alive, but they are adapting to our ways in an organic fashion, and we to theirs. They and we are becoming functionally interdependent. More importantly, they are changing consciousness. I can pull a device out of my pocket right now and watch a typhoon travel across the Philippines. On the same device I can see a traffic jam in Moscow or Bangkok. My father could not do that. I could not do it a few years ago. What we see, how we work, how we meet people, and how we know what is happening around us have all changed. We are very rapidly becoming an entirely new form of life.

Making Sense of Collective Consciousness

We should be trying to make sense of what is happening to us. We should be trying to make sense of collective consciousness and how it is evolving in our midst. The question is more than academic—more than a matter of intellectual interest—it is a question of how we, as collectivized humans, will adapt to a world that has never seen anything like us. To explore the question, we begin with assumptions.

When you arrive at a point where you cannot make sense of a situation, you do well to look at the mindset through which you are approaching it. This holds true for science as well as for everyday life. If you cannot find your car keys and cannot figure out why they are not where you thought they would be, you do well go back and reevaluate the assumptions behind your thinking. You often find a solution to a problem if you change the way you look at it.

Here are three assumptions underlying the relationship between the physical world and consciousness:

The first assumption is that the material world exists whether or not we experience it. I have discussed this already, but it is important to re-emphasize that we assume, especially in the Western tradition, that matter is more fundamental than experience. This assumption stands in the way of understanding both individual and collective consciousness. Physicists, generally the most hardheaded of scientists, do not like flowery ideas about consciousness, emotions, dreams, imaginations and so forth. They claim to concentrate only on what can be known with certainty, but belief in material substance is so deeply buried in the unconscious that few physicists recognize it is an assumption.

Though it remains a pillar of the Western tradition, this assumption is beginning to be questioned by physicists themselves. In the last hundred years it has become increasingly evident that physicists cannot speak of material objects existing independently of observation (conscious experience). Some physicists are beginning to question what they mean by *matter*, though most consider the question too "philosophical" for consideration.

The second assumption is that consciousness exists *inside* of individual people. As you talk to people around you and watch how they move and how their eyes react to what you say, it appears as though they are conscious the same way you feel you are conscious. You assume that their consciousness and yours are separate in space and that each is a separate entity. There is no real evidence for this assumption, however, because you do not see them seeing, you do not hear them hearing, you do not feel them touching. What you actually experience is information from them that coordinates in space and time with what you see and hear and touch directly.

When you hear another person describe a scene, you can verify what they say they are seeing by seeing the same thing directly. This seems to indicate, but does not prove, the independent existence of the scene. When I say there is a dog right now two houses down on the other side of the street, you know where to look. If you turn your head that way you will experience the dog at that location in the visual realm. The order in the sounds I make with my mouth coordinates in space-time with the visual realm of perception. In the commonsense understanding we would say, "Of course you see the dog there because that is where it is, whether or not anyone is looking." But actual experience is limited to the dimensional coordination of the observational information with the visual image. We do not need a separate consciousness for you and for me. Collective consciousness is not separate from visual; the observational realm is experienced directly, alongside the visual.

This leads directly to the third assumption, perhaps the most deeply rooted: the persistent belief that consciousness is the same as self. We speak of what "I experience," or "she sees," or "you hear," assuming all the while that perceptual consciousness is a function of myself, herself, or yourself. Language is built on this assumption. But consciousness is not myself or yourself—not the seer or the seen—it is the *seeing*. Consciousness is not a subject witnessing an object. It is experience. Without assumptions conditioning the experience, there is no duality between subject and object, self and world, spirit and matter, or religion and science.

Dualities, or parallel realities, are built into commonsense thinking. We hold on to irreconcilable truths, even as a unified understanding of conscious experience is trying to present itself. What we call *individual* experience is perceptual consciousness. Collective consciousness is largely the observational realm. Observational *information*, the raw material of collective consciousness, is experienced through the perceptual realms, mostly the auditory and visual. The wholeness of collective consciousness is built, then, of perceptual parts. (Collective consciousness also includes *conceptual* communication from observers: information that is not potential perception.)

We do not understand collective consciousness because we do not understand individual consciousness. Each is, in fact, a level of experience connected to the other. Individual consciousness is not separate from the world—not separate from other consciousness—and collective consciousness is not many individual consciousnesses added together. Everyone experiences both levels directly, all the time. Collective consciousness is seeing through the eyes of another: experiencing the world through a medium, be it electronic or linguistic. Collective consciousness is a level built on top of a perceptual foundation.

The Screen (in its photon, quantum, and observational manifestations) becomes a unified non-dualistic experience of consciousness consistent with what is known of the physical world through quantum mechanics, relativity theory, and everyday life. The Screen is an understanding that begins and ends with experience as the ultimate reality. The apparent separation between you and me, and between individual and collective consciousness, is separate levels of the same fundamental reality: separate but connected realms within a single unified consciousness.

The quantum screen eliminates the concept of matter, but it does not eliminate the physical world. The physical world remains. We still experience it. I see the dog across the street. I hear it there. You say you see and hear it there, too. All of these experiences coordinate in space and time. The difference between the Box and the Screen lies in understanding the coordination to be a structure of consciousness and not of a reality external to consciousness.

When you look out the window, the Earth looks flat. There is nothing wrong with understanding the Earth to be flat so long as you do not travel very far. But if you go an extreme distance in any direction, you will come to realize, in time, that the Earth is easier to understand when it is no longer flat.

As Eastern and Western traditions come together in the world, it becomes plain that neither tradition is wrong or right. The West has concentrated on knowledge within the dimensions, and the East on non-duality. Western science has outgrown its dualistic foundation and now requires an Eastern approach to understand its own discoveries.

Responsibility and Collective Consciousness

Where does responsibility come into collective consciousness? Is collective consciousness something just happening to us, something beyond our control? Are we passive witnesses, or is this evolutionary process something we have decided to do?

Collective consciousness happens without our consent, without our control, and even without our knowledge. "Progress" creates itself. Inventions pop up here and there: cars, washing machines, telephones, computers, the Internet, and the hydrogen bomb. We do not ask them to come, but they show up and we invite them in. We do not know what we are getting ourselves into, but we like what we see at the time, and invite it into our lives. We have not asked to evolve into something larger than individual organisms, but we are evolving nevertheless. Technology has transformed how we see and hear and think, and has expanded our collective presence to the point where we no longer fit easily on the Earth. Responsibility comes in now, when we begin to see what has happened to us. We did not ask for responsibility, but it is ours.

Growth cannot continue unconsciously. There is not enough water, air, or land for endless expansion. Collective responsibility is an adaptation to new conditions. It is a function of the form of life we have become.

Responsibility can be avoided by thinking of the living world as a complexity of mechanical processes—as material stuff, external to ourselves, available for our manipulation and use. This is an understanding fostered by, but not necessary to, Western science. It is not universally human.

While conducting research for a book I was writing on the Keystone XL pipeline a few years ago (*The Pipeline and the Paradigm: Keystone XL, Tar Sands, and the Battle to Defuse the Carbon Bomb*; Ruka Press, 2013), I traveled to the tar sands fields of northern Alberta. I came to know a number of Cree and Dene people there who were appalled by what they saw happening to the land around them. Millions of acres of arboreal forest were being slashed and bulldozed and the soil shoveled away to access oil-rich tar sands beneath the surface. The living world was being torn to pieces and shipped away for consumption in far off places. Huge lakes of toxic waste were left behind. The indigenous people considered this murder and genocide. "How can you reach into the body," one woman said to me, "and tear out the heart of the Earth?"

For those of us of European descent, it is fashionable to think of the Earth as alive. A living Earth justifies environmental awareness and harkens to our poetic side. Within the scientific community, the Gaia theory helps us think in terms of larger living systems. This is a good beginning, but a beginning only. What impresses me about the Cree and Dene is that a living Earth is not a supposition or a theory; it is something they know and feel, something they think without having to think about it. It is an unconditioned view of the world. People who live close to the Earth do not have to be told the land is alive, the forest is alive, the water is alive, and the weather is alive. These things are plain to see. The living wholeness of the Earth is a revelation only to those who live apart from the land—to those of us who have been taught to see pieces of the larger picture and not the picture itself.

The Cree and Dene are modern people; they use computers, carry cell phones and dress in Western style. Many of them now live in cities; they are part of the collectivity. But their cultural traditions keep them close to the earth. As demand for fossil fuel escalates in other parts of the world, they see their land destroyed and their rivers polluted. They see fish in their rivers disfigured by toxins in the water. In their everyday lives they see what humanity is doing and does not see. They sense the natural world at the outer membrane of society. Their voice is not loud, yet we must listen to know what we are doing.

Those of us raised in cities by parents raised in cities have a harder time seeing the life in natural systems. Some of us look at the boreal forest in Alberta as a barrier to the wealth below. The trees are not hard to remove, the soil can be pushed aside, and toxic mine tailings can be dumped into holding ponds above the riverbank. Material objects, living or otherwise, exist to be manipulated for the further progress of humanity.

• • •

Collective consciousness without awareness of the living world becomes mindless and unprincipled economic growth.

Earth care is new to humanity. A generation ago we did not worry about the oceans and forests, icecaps or climate. We did not know they are alive. As the super-organism of humanity pushes to the limits of life on earth, the soft voice of indigenous peoples becomes the wisdom of the age.

Collective consciousness is to individual consciousness as organic consciousness is to cellular consciousness.

Your body and brain are trillions of individual cells. Your experience as an organism is the collective experience of the cells in your body.

Some cells specialize into sensory organs: the retina in your eye, the cochlea of your ear, the tongue in your mouth, the olfactory organ in your nose, or the nerve ending in your finger. Sensory cellular experience is relayed to the central nervous system in the form of information that, combined with information from other sensory cells, becomes a complexity beyond the experience of an individual cell. Visual consciousness, for instance, is the experience of about a million retinal cells, each directly connected to the optic lobe of the brain. Each cell experiences a tactile sensation it relays to the optic lobe in the form of a photon. Each photon combines with a million or so other photons to form a picture in the visual realm of consciousness, a complexity beyond the capacity of an individual cell to experience. Retinal cells do not *see*.

Vision is *reducible* to the tactile experience of a million or so cells in each retina. In this sense *seeing* is "nothing more" than tactile experience. This is, of course, a ridiculously reductive statement, like saying a forest is "nothing more" than trees, or a building is "nothing more" than the bricks of which it is made. The forest is a living system over and above its individual trees, and the building an architecture over and above its component parts. In the same way, vision is a reality over and above the tactile experience of retinal cells. Tactile reduction of photons tells us about the structure of vision—it tells us why light can be either wave or particle—but tactile experience is not the full reality of vision.

Light is the collective consciousness of cells. It is a complexity over and above the consciousness of individual cells, but it is not other than the consciousness of individual cells. Light is not between cells or within one cell or a special group of cells; it is the collective experience of the organism as a whole. The dimensional structure of the photon screen creates the experience of vision. Similarly, collective human consciousness is not within one human or group of humans; it is the collective experience of everyone, as structured by linguistic and electronic media. Media shape the structure of collective consciousness the way dimensions shape the structure of organic consciousness.

As individuals, we experience much of what is happening in society as a whole. Through electronic and other media, each of us has some grasp of the larger picture. But this is changing rapidly. Knowledge and experience are becoming so specialized that an understanding of society as a whole is increasingly difficult to attain. A full holistic understanding may now be beyond individual comprehension. Collective consciousness among people is taking on a life of its own, evolving to a level over and above the experience of individuals.

This sounds scary. It *is* scary—but only if individual experience is the ultimate reality, which it is not. If "we" are each a separate consciousness, then yes, "we" are being taken over by something larger than ourselves. But if "we" are the collectivity of family, community, nation, and humanity, "we" are simply becoming more tightly organized. We will never lose our ability to perceive individually, any more than the multi-cellular organism loses its ability to experience the chemo-tactile realms of cellular perception, but through linguistic and electronic media we will continue to evolve into a form of life that thinks collectively and senses the world collectively. The observational realm of consciousness will continue to grow, and with it other new realms of collective consciousness.

• • •

Religion fosters the evolution of collective from individual consciousness. We learn to equate perceptual and observational experience by worshiping together and learning to see through the eyes of others. Morality is the growth of community. Doing unto others as we would have them do to us is the full transcendence of self.

The difference now is that no one is outside the fold. Electronic media, particularly visual media, transcend culture, language, ideology, and nationality. Religion and morality apply everywhere and to everyone. The principles of religion—any religion—apply beyond the particular cultures in which they have arisen. Jesus, Buddha, Mohammad, Confucius, Lao-Tse, and Moses each spoke to his own culture through the languages and media available at the time; but each, I believe, would have spoken to humanity as a whole had the media of the day made it possible to do so.

The universal collective consciousness rising among people is the spiritual unity of humanity. From within, it is recognition of a common worth regardless of nationality or station in life. From without, it is knowledge and capacity to act in wholeness in relation to the forests, the oceans, the land, and the weather.

— 7 —

THE IMPORTANCE OF THE QUANTUM SCREEN

The quantum screen model takes consciousness out of the dimensions. That is the paradigm shift. Consciousness inside space and time is divided into you and me and every other individual. Consciousness outside the dimensions is a single reality.

But why spend such great effort describing the quantum screen as a model for perceptual consciousness? Why is it important... or is it important? Is it only an intellectual exercise?

I developed this model to reconcile a fundamental division in the Western mind underlying the scientific tradition—the division between object and subject, between the world and the self. I believe this division is not inherent in nature, but arises in the human mind at a fundamental level. The division—the duality—shows up in the manner in which we try to understand physical enigmas at the extremes of dimensional experience. It also shows up in everyday living. We think we are separate beings, separate from the world and separate from each other.

Many people are capable of wonder, know they are alive, and experience the unity of life directly from time to time. Some have experienced a glimpse of the living reality beyond the separation of self and world, mind and body, seer and seen. They know the miracle of being; and they sense the sheer excitement of seeing, touching, feeling, and thinking. Many people have experienced something like this sometime in life. But often, the next day, the same people are unable to reconcile their experience with what they see in everyday life. They see divisions between one thing and another, between one person and another. The world appears to be divided on a fundamental level, on the physical level, and their experience of unity becomes a passing illusion—a fleeting euphoria without basis in the real world. The unity that seems a full reality in its own moment becomes a sentimental memory in the next. Through the quantum screen I hope to show that unity is more than a sentiment, more than a poetic fantasy: that unity underlies all experience—perceptual, conceptual, and collective—on a profound physical level, and that its existence is consistent with modern science.

All experience is fundamentally spiritual.

There is no private atmosphere, no private ocean for individuals or nations. There is no defense of any part of the Earth against any other. There is no room for division. There is only a united humanity in relation to nature and to itself. If we are to continue our lives on Earth, we will relate in wholeness to the streams and oceans, to the land and forests and fields, and to the atmosphere and weather and climate. We will feel the pulse of streams, the bones of rock, and the breath of trees. That is the way we will live.

PART II

Retain the word matter, and apply it to the objects of sense, if you please; provided you do not attribute to them any subsistence distinct for their being perceived.

—George Berkeley

— 8 —

MY STORY:
AN AUTOBIOGRAPHICAL SKETCH

My parents were both chemists. For as long as I can remember, science was the preferred topic of discussion at the dinner table. As an older child, a great broadening occurred in my mind when I prepared a school project with the help of my mother on the protein synthesis of DNA. The mechanism by which living things grew, I learned, was the combining of amino acids into proteins as directed by the blueprint of the DNA molecule. I had always thought that God made this sort of thing happen, but saw, through this experience with my mother, that chemistry provided a more intricately detailed explanation.

The Tension Between Science and Religion

Where science is able to explain how things happen, religion explains what they are. I never thought either was ultimately right, but always felt the tension between them. Throughout my adolescent life I alternated between being very religious or very scientific, but eventually came to see that religion and science are two different means of poking into the same reality.

Science goes only so far. It cannot tell you what life is; it can only tell you how parts of life interact. Physics is the study, through cause and effect, of how and why things move around and bump into each other. It's a good tool in its place, but when I studied physics on the university level, I saw that where cause and effect explain the parts, they do not explain the whole. When two billiard balls collide, science can tell you exactly what will happen to each of them. But we make the mistake of assuming that there are smaller and smaller billiard balls on smaller and smaller scales, bouncing against each other, making things happen on the atomic level. It turns out that when you get down to the level of atoms and subatomic particles, those tiny billiard balls are not solid. They pass right through each other and do not exist in space and time in any absolute sense. And they depend for their existence on whether or not someone is watching them! Below the quantum level cause and effect are not revealed in the hard facts of science, but in mathematical probabilities. Space and time are no longer the fundamental structures of a rigid external universe.

But science is not invalidated by its limits. I have come to understand science not as an absolute truth, but as a way of understanding the world on the collective level. It is not the world itself; it is a special structure of consciousness.

In the late 1960s, in college, I studied both physics and philosophy, and encountered the limitations of both disciplines. I did not want to become a physicist, and though I identified with philosophy, I did not want to study it on the university level. In philosophy courses it seemed we were not studying philosophy; we were studying *about* philosophy. We were learning about what other people thought—mostly dead German guys—and what they had to say about the world. That was interesting enough, but I wanted to look at the world itself. What's going on right now? What are we seeing? What is this life? A seminal event in my life was a paper I wrote on the concept of matter. Matter, I decided, did not exist independently of consciousness, but was what I called an agreement of perceptions. The difference between matter and illusion is touching and seeing (or smelling, tasting, hearing) an object at the same time. I did not realize until much later how this observation would become the core of my world view.

In physics we learned that matter is not a true substance, but a form of condensed energy. This got me thinking. We also learned that dimensions became distorted at high velocities and blend into one another on the subatomic level. It occurred to me that space and time dimensions might be structures of human consciousness, not something out there. I knew then there was something about physics that had a strong connection to philosophy, but I didn't know what it was, and at the time I had other things I needed to do with my life. I needed to graduate from college and stay out of the army! So I put the physics/philosophy connection on the shelf, promising myself I would get back to it later. It was twenty years later that I realized that the "agreement" of perceptions underlying the concept of matter was based in a dimensional context; that is, that what defines a material object is seeing and touching at the same point in space and time. This is where the concept of matter comes from. Dimensions are the structure of perceptual consciousness.

Physics and philosophy, like science and religion, did not differ in the world; they differed only as separate approaches to the world. Maybe this is why I never ended up in academia. I would never fit into any academic department. A direct approach to nature, I found a year later, was through meditation, and I began meditating before I knew what I was doing. I would sit still and just look at what was going on in my mind. When I found out that people on the other side of the world had been doing this for thousands of years, I decided to major in religion. I resolved the difference between science and religion by transcending the difference between them.

Activism

I was not an activist in my early years at Oberlin College. During the Vietnam war, when I was a freshman, two navy recruiters showed up on campus provoking a big street demonstration with police and tear gas. A crowd of students surrounded the recruiters and refused to let them out of their car. I found myself fascinated by the scene, but did not become one of the demonstrators, choosing instead to witness the spectacle from the safety of several hundred feet. I had always felt that I could see what was going on better from a distance—from an objective viewpoint—without becoming involved in one side or the other. I was above the fray.

I was not entirely opposed to the Vietnam war. I could see both sides of the issue. There was the need to defend our country and to do so before it became a wider conflict, to contain the worldwide spread of communism the way our parents generation had prevented the spread of fascism. I was not opposed to the student movement either, I just had no need for it.

Then I went to Bolivia. I had a true immersion experience in another place and culture and saw the world from an entirely different point of view. It was a huge experience for me. When I returned, I saw the American involvement in Vietnam from a totally new perspective. I realized how horribly wrong that war was. I had not been able to see its awful injustice from the American point of view, but I could see it plain as day from the human point of view. This was a classical paradigm shift. What changed was not the war; what changed was me. The difference was not in what I was looking at, but where I was looking from. I realized that the objective distance I had prided myself in was keeping me from living in the world, and that I had to get involved to be a living person, even though I might pay an intellectual price for losing that objectivity. So I began to act, to be a full human being in the world, to get out there and do what was right. The need to feel what people were feeling—American, Bolivian, Vietnamese, or Cambodian—eventually overwhelmed the need for intellectual objectivity. I have been an activist ever since.

When I fight for peace, I know there is a contradiction. I know there are other points of view in which I am absolutely wrong. Yet I must act. I have to advocate for peace, and for the natural world. Rather than be objective, and safe, I have found it more important to be part of the fight. I have rolled up my sleeves and jumped into the trenches!

— 9 —

ENERGY AND THE
COLLECTIVE SELF

What sort of *doing* might proceed from a vision of the quantum screen? The Screen is an abstract concept, a model of perceptual consciousness, and an understanding of the physical in relation to the spiritual world. It is not a creed or an ideology. There is nothing political about it. How, then, does the quantum screen lead to action?

Clearly, a vision of the quantum screen does not reveal any particular course of action. But in showing a continuum between individual and collective consciousness, it reveals how humanity is likely to evolve in adapting to new conditions. The Screen shows the perceptual realms are not other than the observational—individual consciousness is not separate from collective. Collective consciousness is humanity as we are now, and as we are becoming. The observational realm is built from the raw material of everyday experience. It is not a looming foreign presence. It is available to everyone, everywhere; and it is how we, as humans, will experience life on Earth in the coming years. Through collective consciousness—and collective self—humanity will emerge (or not emerge) from the current crises.

The quantum screen does not show anything in particular. It shows actual events, whatever they may be, within a matrix of interlocking dimensional potentials. It presents a picture, but no particular picture. The structure of the Screen allows for the gradual evolution of observational from perceptual consciousness: of collective from individual consciousness. The Screen model is a vehicle through which we may understand what is happening to us and to other forms of life as we face an insecure future.

This much—the evolution of collective consciousness—is happening largely without our deliberate input. But collective consciousness alone is not enough. Survival will not follow mere acknowledgment of the Screen; survival will require collective *action* appropriate to new realities experienced on the Screen. Survival will require the rise of a universal collective self.

One reality for human survival is the necessity of conversion from fossil fuel energy to renewable energy. The need for renewable energy in the very near future will inspire a new practical order of collective human behavior appropriate to the emerging realities of life on Earth.

Human civilization is in a stage of adolescence, moving in the general direction of adulthood. We have responsibilities now that we did not have before. We used to live only for ourselves; now we live for trees and flowers, for fish and birds, for worms and insects, and for beasts of the field. We used not to worry about the oceans, the atmosphere, or the forests. Nature took care of herself. Nature took care of us. Now, nature needs us. She needs us because we have become so large a force in the living world that we will take much of life with us, whatever we do. We are a new direction life is taking: a new experiment life is trying. Nature has invested millions of years of evolution in our success, but her investment in us will not succeed without our intention.

Life on Earth began by harnessing chemical energy from soil and seawater, but life soon came to require more energy than could be harvested sustainably from earth-based chemical reactions. Light from the sun proved a more reliable, renewable, and abundant source of energy. An early form of bacterium learned that by harnessing sunshine, it could separate oxygen from carbon and hydrogen, storing energy in carbohydrate "batteries." The energy could be released at any later time by recombining carbohydrate with oxygen. Billions of years ago, this photosynthesizing bacterium was incorporated into larger cells in the form of chloroplasts. Millions of years ago, complex photosynthesizing cell communities grew leaves and stems to become the plant kingdom—the living architecture of solar energy collection.

Should life evolve to the next level it will look again for energy beyond the Earth. There is not enough fuel in carbohydrate (and hydrocarbon) chemistry for the long-term needs of life in its industrial form. There is not enough air to absorb carbon waste. The byproduct of carbon combustion is already distorting the atmospheric chemistry of the entire planet. Life, to live, will harness human civilization to harvest energy directly from the sun. Humanity will evolve beyond earth-based chemistry.

Humanity is not moving in this direction now. We live and die by coal, oil, and natural gas. Without these, there would be nothing recognizable about our civilization. We rely on carbon energy for nearly everything we do, and have no big plans to rely on anything else. Carbon fuel flows through the pipes and wires and highways of our cities. We use it for light, heat, communication, transportation, and entertainment. We use it to cultivate, fertilize, package, and market the food we eat. Fossil carbon fuel is the present reality of human civilization, yet it cannot and will not support human civilization in the future. There will be no human future with fossil fuel. None. The only possibility for humanity is a transition to renewable energy.

Running out of fuel is not the problem. A generation ago we thought there was not enough fuel. The energy crisis of the twentieth century was thought to be a planetary shortage of petroleum; but we now know there were, and are, huge reserves of oil, coal and natural gas across the earth—more fuel by far than we can ever use. The crisis in the later twentieth century was a disturbance in the *market* for oil. But since then new deposits have been discovered as quickly as old deposits have been depleted. New extraction techniques bring more fuel to the surface than ever before. Fossil fuel remains a finite resource—there is only so much in the ground—but there is three to five times more in the ground than we will need to despoil the atmosphere. We will not run out. The problem is not too little fossil fuel. The problem is too much.

The problem would be simpler if we were running out. If there were not enough fossil fuel to go around, prices would rise with scarcity. Higher prices would force conservation and stepped-up research into alternatives: solar, wind, wave, and geothermal, as well as other technologies we cannot imagine now. As renewable energy became cheaper than fossil fuel, the transition would happen on its own. We would not have to think it through. Supply and demand would force the change, not governmental action. This would be easier. There would be no need to decide, as a civilization, to make the transition.

The market does not require consciousness. It does not require us to think; it only requires us to follow our economic noses. When fossil fuel is available, the market directs us towards consuming it. When it is not, the market directs us elsewhere. The market does not see the bigger picture. It does not see oil spills, strip mines, exploding tanker cars, or carbon building up in the atmosphere. The market reduces collective responsibility to individual behavior. It does not know what it is doing. It does not show us that we, the consumers, are the ones spilling the oil and polluting the air. The market does not remind us of the consequences of our purchase when we stop at the gas pump. Many of us who are aware of the consequences blame the people who extract and sell the fuel, but these people extract and sell only what we buy.

Humanity will have to decide to make the transition to renewable energy for reasons other than economic. The market will not help us this time. It will not tell us what to do. After the transition, after we have consciously decided how best to live on the earth in a practical and peaceful manner, market forces will be in effect, but they will no longer direct the overall course of human development. They will operate within a world view larger than themselves. Supply and demand will find a place within the larger context of global ecology. We will decide to live—then decide how to allocate resources. We will choose to live whether or not it is cheaper.

The triumph of consciousness over economic blindness will depend on a much higher general awareness of how the earth's atmosphere is changing. Awareness is arising, but only gradually. The side effects of carbon combustion are barely perceptible today, and will not be visible in everyday life for years to come. There will be storms, floods, and fires; but there have always been storms, floods, and fires, and it will be hard to tell if these are worse than before. Sea levels will rise, but only inches over decades and centuries. Temperatures will rise, but only slightly. The difference between a 100-degree summer afternoon and a 103.6-degree summer afternoon is barely perceptible. Higher temperatures at night and in winter will be even less noticeable, and in some climates higher temperatures will be welcomed. Individual human bodies do not sense average temperatures, floods, or rises in sea level. We will know there is a difference in climate only through long-range scientific observation—that is, through the observational realm of consciousness. We will know what is happening collectively, and not individually.

We will know that the storms, floods, fires, heat waves and famines are out of the ordinary because other people—thousands of other people—have measured and recorded storms and floods and heat waves at millions of times and places in the past. We will know that what we are witnessing is out of the ordinary because we will know what the ordinary is. Base-line averages are known through long-term studies. We will see collectively what we cannot see individually.

Through collective consciousness we will know that life on Earth is changing. The *information* will be perceptual; we will see and hear through quanta, but the images will be observational. Carbon dioxide, for instance, is colorless and odorless—there is virtually no way to perceive it—yet it is carbon dioxide that plays the starring role in climate change. We know about carbon dioxide through science. Even climate itself is an observational image. Climate is not perceivable; when you step outdoors you do not see climate—you see weather. Climate is *average* weather, known through many time-separated and space-separated observations. As climate disruption affects the viability of human life, humanity will evolve a more intense and immediate experience of the observational realm of consciousness. We will experience collectively a world we cannot perceive individually. We will become aware of the climate around us through the sensory organs of electronic media.

Here are some things we know already: 150 years ago, when humanity first began burning coal in a big way, the atmospheric level of carbon-dioxide stood at about 280 parts per million. The level now (2016) is about 400 parts per billion, an increase of 42.8%. This is not a marginal increase. It is not a local irregularity. This is a major change in the chemistry of the *entire* atmosphere. Every cubic foot of air has 42.8% more carbon than it had before the beginning of the fossil fuel era. This is a shift in the whole planetary system: there is no place on Earth with a preindustrial atmosphere. The additional atmospheric carbon will change the intensity of storm systems. It will change where and when it rains or does not rain. It will change worldwide agricultural production in ways that cannot be predicted. And it will diminish the diversity of life.

We also know that the fossil fuels at our disposal contain three to five times more carbon than would be needed to raise the Earth's average temperature two degrees centigrade (3.6 degrees Fahrenheit). Two degrees is the generally agreed allowable limit for global warming. Climate disaster may happen at two degrees, or five degrees, or 1.5 degrees: no one knows. But we do know the more carbon-based fuel we use, the hotter it gets; and the hotter it gets, the closer we get to a runaway climate. There is plenty of fuel to make it happen.

No one knows what will happen beyond a two-degree increase. World leaders would like to keep temperatures below that limit because scientists suspect that hotter temperatures increase the risk of runaway global warming. The climate becomes "runaway" when it continues to get hotter and hotter on its own—without further fossil fuel combustion. There is a threshold beyond which temperatures will increase on their own no matter how we try to stop them. This would happen through what are called *positive feedback loops*. A positive feedback loop is a change in a dynamic system that causes further change in the same direction. (A *negative* feedback loop causes *less* change in the same direction.) The Earth's climate is a complex system of many feedback loops, both positive and negative. For global warming, the most troublesome are the positive. Here are a few examples:

The albedo effect: Ice reflects sunlight back into space, keeping the Earth cool, but dark seawater absorbs solar energy, heating the Earth. As the Earth warms, more sea ice melts, exposing more dark ocean water to sunlight, further warming the Earth. The hotter it is; the hotter it gets.

The photosynthetic effect: Droughts, floods, fires, and high temperatures all reduce photosynthesis, and thus plant growth. Less plant growth means less carbon dioxide extraction from the air, more greenhouse effect, and more warming. The hotter it is; the hotter it gets.

The tundra effect: Millions of tons of greenhouse gases like methane and carbon dioxide are trapped in frozen tundra soils. As the Earth warms, soils thaw, releasing more greenhouse gases, which further warm the Earth and thaw more frozen tundra soil. The hotter it gets; the hotter it gets.

The gas hydrate effect: Millions more tons of carbon-based greenhouse gases are trapped in gas hydrates in deep ocean deposits. These probably contain more carbon than all the coal, oil, and natural gas in the world. It would take high threshold temperatures to release these gases, but their presence in the atmosphere would make life difficult or impossible for most species now inhabiting the land or the oceans. The hotter it gets, the closer we come to mass extinction.

There are also negative feedback loops. For instance, the more carbon there is in the atmosphere, the more leaves and stems grow to absorb it. Other factors being equal, plants put on significantly more growth when more carbon dioxide is in the air. The more plants grow, the more carbon is extracted from the air, and the cooler the Earth gets. But other factors are not equal. A lot of global warming might be offset by increased photosynthesis were it not for the fact that floods, droughts, fires, and higher temperatures are decreasing plant growth at the same time. Tropical rain forests are being cut down at a rate much faster than could be offset by marginally increased plant growth from higher carbon levels. In the deep geological past, global warming episodes were often counter balanced by tropical forest growth spreading north and south from equatorial into temperate regions; but that is not happening this time around.

The climate is an extremely complex system with trends and feedbacks and counter trends and counter feedbacks. Climates have remained relatively stable over millions of years due to the self-correcting complexity of interacting factors. But there have been times when one factor or another has deviated so far from normal that the entire climate has shifted dramatically. 750 million years ago the Earth grew extremely cold with polar ice caps reaching the tropics, reflecting sunlight back into space. Only a narrow band of open ocean water remained at the equator. 250 million years ago, temperatures soared and oceans flooded the continents. Ninety percent of living species died on land and in the sea. We cannot say for sure what caused these extreme imbalances, or what might cause them again. The next shift may be quite small. There is no certainty of any particular scenario, only an increased probability of imbalance with increased carbon levels in the air. The goal of keeping average global temperature from rising above two degrees is to avoid triggering a feedback loop that may raise temperatures high enough to trigger another feedback loop, and so on. Once runaway climate begins, there is no way to stop it.

No one can say that there will or will not be climate disaster in the mid to late twenty-first century, and certainly no one would want to trigger mass extinction just as his or her great-grandchildren were setting up house. But climate disaster could happen. If the situation were clear, if the cause and effect were more mechanically determinate, everyone would know now is the time to stop all use of coal, oil, and natural gas. Everyone would do whatever had to be done. But the situation is not clear. There are only probabilities, and even the probabilities are unsure. Global climate change remains distant and hypothetical in the public mind. Some people point to storms and floods and heat waves and say, "This is it! Here it comes!" Others say these are just storms and floods and heat waves—a little worse than normal, maybe. Each sees what he or she is disposed to see. Climate change becomes a matter of "belief."

There is no doubt, however, that people are the cause of the current climate imbalance. Carbon levels are way up, warming is up, carbon is causing the warming, and people put the carbon in the air. It is as plain as day. We are the culprits. Yet—and this is an important point—we are not to blame. Humanity did not decide to begin burning fossil fuels. There was no conscious choice two hundred years ago to interact with the climate. It just happened. Life was experimenting—with us. Life was taking a new overall evolutionary direction—playing an entirely new game—and passed the ball to us.

Two hundred years later, life is not through with its experiment. It is still waiting to see how we will run with the ball. Will we keep running without looking where we are going, or will we adapt ourselves to a newer, larger ecological niche?

Reacting to climate change will be a collective response. We are all in the atmosphere together. It does not matter that carbon comes from you or from me, from China, the United States, or Botswana; it all goes into the air: everybody's air. Race, religion, ideology, and nationality make no difference. Unlike any crisis in the past—political, economic, military, or environmental—the climate crisis is truly global. It is not only collective; it is *universally* collective. It involves all people everywhere. The only effective response will be from the whole from everybody, everywhere. A positive response from any subgroup of humans—any nation or group of nations—no matter how conscientious, will never be enough. Life's experiment with us will require a new level of universal response: collective doing on a global scale. Nothing like this has happened before. This will be an evolutionary departure; no living form in the nearly four-billion-year history of life on Earth has ever evolved into a universal collectivity.

We are aware of the climate through science, through observational consciousness. Observation is *potential perception*: communicated information that anyone *could* see, hear, smell, taste, or touch directly under the same conditions. What a scientist says he sees is tested and re-tested, becoming potentially perceivable by anyone anywhere, whether or not they actually perceive it. Science is what we know together. But science, particularly climate science, remains an intellectual construction based on probabilities. Are we to change the foundation of civilization on the basis of what *might* happen? The change in awareness will happen when potential perception becomes actual: when large numbers of people *see* the storms and floods and fires for themselves, when agricultural production drops and people *feel* it drop. When distant probabilities become first-hand realities, observational consciousness will be as clear as perceptual. At that point we will act.

But when will that be? The symptoms of climate chaos will be plain to see just before, or just after, it is too late to do anything about them. It may be too late already. We do not know when too late is. The oceans absorb carbon dioxide and only gradually release it back into the atmosphere, so the carbon we put in the atmosphere today may not affect the climate for thirty years or more. This dampens the immediate effect of atmospheric emissions on the climate, but the slow release of carbon from the oceans will make the climate worse for a generation or so after we stop burning fossil fuel. How bad will it be by then, and how much worse will it get before temperatures level off? The only certainties will be retrospective: if we convert to renewables too soon, we will not be sure action was necessary; if we convert too late, we will have the assurance that it was.

What are the chances we will avoid the two-degree limit? Near zero. If all burning of all fossil fuels were to end tomorrow morning, there would be a chance of staying below two degrees; but that is not going to happen. Average temperatures have already risen by nearly one degree, and will keep rising for thirty years or so after we stop adding new carbon. As temperatures continue to rise, we will get close to the two-degree limit even with little or no new carbon. Our parent's and grandparent's carbon emissions in the past have raised temperatures the first degree, and our emissions now will raise it another degree or so for our children and grandchildren. The new carbon we emit in the coming decades will raise temperatures even higher for our great grandchildren. We will get to two degrees, and more. Then what?

There is little effect we can have as individuals. We can switch out light bulbs, recycle cans, walk to work, and install solar panels. These are all necessary, but society as a whole has to make the change. We will be effective only in acting collectively. Walking to the store or turning the thermostat down is "doing your part," but in a society whose infrastructure is built on petroleum and natural gas, there will be times when you have to drive to the store and times when you have to turn up the furnace to keep from freezing. Individual behavior is important, especially as a first step, but ultimately it is *infrastructure* that will have to change. Existing infrastructure—gas lines, oil wells, refineries, coal mines, gasoline engines, furnaces, diesel trucks—will continue to be used because they are there. It is hard not to use what already exists. But they should not be replaced when they wear out. *New* fossil fuel

infrastructure should not be built: no new pipelines, strip mines, oil tankers, refineries, fracking wells, tar sands mines, and mountaintop removal sites! No new fossil fuel infrastructure! We should stop building new systems that will burden our children and grandchildren with the carbon habit. We can only hope that we have not already irreparably damaged the climate for them. Fossil fuel infrastructure should be replaced only with renewable energy infrastructure. This is something we can all do now, together. But to be effective, we must act collectively and universally.

This is the hard part—the part we have never done before: we must create a universal collective self. Create new government. Not a new policy of government: a new *level* of government. Government is how we do things collectively. Government is instituted among humans to protect rights and to restrict rights, of both individuals and groups of individuals. In order to protect the inalienable rights of life, liberty, and the pursuit of happiness, government restricts the right to kill, enslave, and steal. In order to protect climate stability, new government will be instituted among men and women to restrict the right to dump carbon into the air. If you think it is your right as a sovereign nation to burn coal because you have it in your mountains or because some other nation burned it a hundred years ago, you will have to stop. If you think it is your right as a private individual to drive a gasoline car or use natural gas-generated electricity, you will have to stop. For the benefit of society as a whole, and for those as yet unborn, you will have to make your way with renewable energy. The demand you create for heat, light, transportation, food, communication, and entertainment will be channeled to technologies that produce energy directly from the sun. There is no other way for life to live. You and I—your national government and mine—we will all have to face up to this reality.

As inefficient, corrupt, and undemocratic as government may be at times, it is how people do things collectively. Government is how we live with each other and how we will act to preserve a stable climate. The form and effectiveness of government is an ongoing question I will not open here. But I will say the shortcomings of government cannot be avoided by avoiding government itself, and extending the scope of government from the national to the universal level will reduce the burden of government by reducing or eliminating the burden of national defense. Of this I am sure.

To do things effectively, government narrows the focus of collective consciousness. It cannot see everything or take every possibility into consideration. Government—good government—looks at the big picture (the observation screen), absorbs as much science as it can stand, then reduces and simplifies the picture to a practical level within the scope of its resources. This is the political process—a form of collective thinking. To make decisions that lead to actions in the real world, government creates a curvature of collective consciousness—a reduction of imagination to a focus of order that can be brought into the physical world. The wave function of possibility collapses into the dimensions. Government thinks of what to do, and does it.

The picture will never be complete. That is why we should not wait to know everything before acting. There will always be doubts, contradictions, and unknowns. Wisdom comes not of certainty, but of choosing which uncertainty to follow. Effective action comes of seeing as much as possible of the big picture and creating practical imagination within it. The picture now forming is a near certainty of runaway climate disaster within the next several decades. We will look, think, and act collectively, and soon.

The climate crisis will stimulate continuing development of observational consciousness. There will be more use of electronic media, more awareness of global trends, and more public discussion of weather events. We will come to see a world picture we cannot see as individuals. This is the continuation of an evolutionary trend towards higher levels of human consciousness, a trend that began thousands of years ago with the rise of symbolic language. While collective consciousness is a form of *being*, collective self is a form of *doing*. Since humanity began, and before, people have cooperated in groups—coming together for common defense, for instance. Collective consciousness and collective self are not new to the present day. But climate response is different. Climate response requires *universal* cooperation. It requires more than coordinated behavior of individuals within a group; it requires coordination of groups within the whole. Effective climate response means nothing less than the cooperation of humanity as a whole.

For the first time in four billion years, life will consciously and deliberately interact with the atmosphere. It will sense the danger and do something about it. Through the agency of human civilization, life will evolve new technologies and new institutional forms of coordinated behavior, learning to tip the carbon balance one way or another in response to climate changes. A universal human self will become a conscious feedback mechanism.

The burden of creating the mechanism for interacting with the climate will fall to humanity. We will form the institutional self that acts for the well-being of the whole. We will do the doing. To ensure climate stability for all, we will regulate our behavior and the behavior of other forms of life incorporated into our economic system.

The economy will continue to grow, but its driving force will not be exclusively economic. Decisions directing the course of economic growth will be made within a value context that includes the life of trees, rivers, plants, and indigenous peoples. Blind market forces will operate within the larger context of global ecology. How will industrial facilities affect land and streams, atmospheric chemistry, ocean temperatures, and the job market? How will new agricultural techniques affect soils, aquifers, carbon emissions, food prices, and rural dislocation? How will new buildings and highways use less energy and create more space for solar collection?

Humanity will follow the plant kingdom in developing a new architecture of solar collection. Buildings and roadways will be designed to gather sunlight, as well as to house and move people. Steel and glass will be stems and leaves. We will grow toward the sun. In time, we will gather sunlight in the deep curvature of space.

Future economic planning will be practical if and only if conceived in a global context based on the long-term interests of life as a whole. The new architecture will rotate into the world we observe, and stay there.

Or will it?

Successful energy conversion is not inevitable. Predictions are notoriously inaccurate, and energy use may continue in the future more or less as it has in the past. There may be less change than I suggest. But from where I can see, climate chaos is a near certainty, and constitutes the first truly global crisis humanity has faced. No individual person or nation can protect its own atmosphere. The pending crisis requires nothing less than deliberate universal action. I welcome this new level of collective living—this new layer of civilization. I believe it is worth a small sacrifice of individual and sovereign rights. Depriving the right to pollute is as vital to civilization as depriving the right to kill and steal. A worldwide means of controlling atmospheric carbon will be a departure from a catastrophic trajectory. It will be a new era in human history.

Or will it?

The human spirit will find a way to live on this small planet, or it will not. Humanity will evolve beyond the individual and the group to the global and the universal. Or it will not. We may prefer our separate parts of humanity. Life's experiment continues. The results will be in soon.

— 10 —

THE FOURTH DIALOGUE:
DOES MATTER EXIST
INDEPENDENTLY OF PERCEPTION?

In 1713, Irish philosopher George Berkeley created the fictional characters Philonous and Hylas to argue the case for immaterialism, or the belief that material substance does not exist independently of perception. Philonous is Berkeley himself, and Hylas the materialist skeptic.

The first three dialogues (those written by Berkeley) take place as the two friends walk through a garden on three successive mornings. Philonous stresses the reality of perceptual experience—of seeing, hearing, touching, tasting, and smelling—but observes that a material substratum supporting perception is purely gratuitous. He considers a cherry along the way:

> *"I see this cherry. I feel it, I taste it: and, I am sure, nothing cannot be seen, or felt, or tasted: it is therefore real. Take away the sensations of softness, moisture, redness, tartness, and you take away the cherry. Since it is not a being distinct from those sensations, a cherry, I say, is nothing but a congeries of sensible impressions, or ideas perceived by various senses: which ideas are united into one thing (or have the same name given them) by the mind; because they are observed to attend each other... But if, by the word cherry, you mean an unknown nature, distinct from all those sensible qualities, and by its existence, something distinct from its being perceived; then, indeed, I own, neither you or I, nor any one else, can be sure it exists."*

At length, Hylas is convinced, but he suggests that the discovery may be semantic:

> *"In denying matter, at first glance I am tempted to imagine, you deny the things we see and feel; but, upon reflexion, find there is no ground for it. What think you, therefore, of retaining the name matter, and applying it to sensible things?"*

Philonous responds:

> *"With all my heart: Retain the word matter, and apply it to the objects of sense, if you please; provided you do not attribute to them any subsistence distinct for their being perceived."*

The Fourth Dialogue

In this Fourth Dialogue (which is my own creation), Philonous and Hylas, having wakened, miraculously, after three hundred years, find themselves once again in the garden. The doctrine of immaterialism has been largely forgotten, and Hylas, the apostate, has slept well. Philonous, on the other hand, has lain awake for "the last third of the night" considering the discoveries of physical science in the twentieth century. He supposes there is new ammunition in his battle against the concept of matter.

Phil. Good morrow, Hylas. It is early and you are already in the garden.

Hyl. I am rarely abroad at this hour. But I slept well—very well—for what seems 300 years and more. We have wakened to a new world.

Phil. So it would seem. I slept intermittently the first part of the night and woke with a start before dawn. I lay awake the last third of the night, struggling to make sense of this new day.

Hyl. Was it our discussion that disturbed you?

Phil. Yes, it was. When I laid my head on the pillow, I thought we had resolved differences in my favor—I felt I had prevailed—but something lingered through the night. As I slept, an erosive force consumed the constructions we had so carefully assembled. When I awoke, there was nothing left, as if our words were swept by the wind. My thoughts had faded in the darkness; I could no longer make them out. When I awoke, finally, a new army of thoughts had invaded...

Hyl. Yes, now that you mention it, it seems that way to me, too. You had me utterly convinced. Everything you said made perfect sense, and I was made a proselyte to your principles. But now, as I stand here, a wave of common sense passes over me. What you said is true, I admit, on the elevated plane of rational discourse; but right here, right now, it does not apply at all. As I kick this little rock out of the path, I hear a slapping sound and see it tumbling into the grass. I feel a stubbing sensation in my toe. There has to be something out there causing me to hear, see, and feel at the same time. This is common sense. Since our discussion, I am sure I don't know what that something is, but I can say without doubt the rock exists. It has to exist! I suppose I could smell and taste it as well, were I to risk an undignified pose.

Phil. You are right, of course, about hearing, seeing, and feeling the rock at the same time. But this does not counter anything I said yesterday. What you say does not prove the existence of matter.

Hyl. No, it does not. But neither does anything you said prove the non-existence of matter.

Phil. I own it.

Hyl. You could go on all day long—which, as I remember, you did—about how I might experience seeing, hearing, and feeling the rock, but never experience the material rock outside of perception. True, there is no experience outside of experience—I do admit that—but there has to be something "out there" coordinating all these separate experiences into a single thing I call the rock! Why not admit that the rock just is? (Or the cherry, more conveniently smelled and tasted.) You spent hours yesterday in this very garden browbeating me into an acceptance of immaterialism, but you never once showed me in any absolute sense why it is better than materialism. You made me doubt matter, but what can you offer to replace it? If there is no compelling evidence either way, I am forced to choose what seems in everyday life to be true.

Phil. Yes, I see what you are saying, Hylas. I do not retract anything I said, but I can see how its impact has diminished with time. And I am sorry for whatever rhetorical tricks I may have used to convince you.

Hyl. I felt I was buying a used car.

Phil. Oh. I didn't mean...

Hyl. Our first author has made you more quick-witted than I. That is not entirely fair in a philosophical discussion such as this.

Phil. Yes, admittedly. But he used me for his own end as much as he did you. I daresay we cannot undo what has been done in this respect without undoing ourselves entirely.

Hyl. True. But a lot has happened since yesterday, and I have come somewhat more into my own, Parmenides notwithstanding. For one thing, I have come to question your use of God.

Phil. "Use" of God? Why, how could a mortal pretend to "use" God?

Hyl. I am saying that you used Him, Philonous. When you could find no better way to explain why I encountered multiple perceptions of the cherry or why multiple observers see the same cherry at the same time, you asked God to clean up the mess you had made. You claimed the cherry existed in His mind, and He made it available to everyone. This strikes me as a weak attempt to explain what we experience.

Phil. I believe this to be the case: there is no such thing as material substance existing independently of perception—there are only ideas and spirit. Everything that exists is in one mind or another. Our minds are limited—we can't experience everything—but God does experience everything, and makes His experiences available to us. This is what I believe, Hylas. It is a beautiful vision, and it does not require us to invent a superfluous universe of material substance.

Hyl. It is a beautiful vision; no one can deny it. Even now, as I consider it, I am in awe. Your vision explains everything; we behold the Creator...

Phil. He did not create something from nothing...

Hyl. But here is my problem: God, you might agree, is where our thinking begins and where it ends. Do you agree?

Phil. Yes, I suppose one could say that.

Hyl. To insert God into your thinking is to admit that you can think no more beyond a certain point. Am I right?

Phil. Yes..., but that...

Hyl. And you are saying no one else can think beyond that point either, unless he is God. It's as if you are putting up a sign: *No Trespassing Beyond This Point.*

Phil. Yes, I recognize the limit of my intellect, and that of others. We cannot presume to know everything. Should we leave no room for God in our understanding?

Hyl. That is just the point: by "leaving room" for God you have put Him in a room. You have created a little space in your system and forced God into it. This is unacceptable for two reasons. First, I am sure God does not appreciate being sent to His room; and second, other thinkers do not appreciate being told when and where to stop thinking.

Phil. Ouch!

Hyl. The vision is beautiful, Philonous. It completes your system with a resounding chord of spiritual affirmation. But I cannot accept it. If we had let God hire angels to push the planets around in their spheres, we would not have needed Universal Gravitation. Do you see? From where I am standing just now, I must believe in the rock. It is what I experience.

Phil. I see, Hylas, that you have recovered from your "browbeating." You express yourself well, and I am taken aback. Alas. But the sun finds us here in the open and the day warms. Let us walk through the long shadows of the morning. The day is in its glory at this hour. Allow me to share the recent thoughts that swarmed my mind upon wakening.

Hyl. Oh, Yes! I nearly forgot. What was this "army of thoughts?" I hope it did not issue from anything I said.

Phil. It did not, Hylas. The thoughts I speak of arose not from yesterday's discussion, but from more recent happenings. I believe certain events since we last spoke have vastly improved my argument.

Hyl. Really! Have you found a proof for the non-existence of matter? I hope you will leave God out of it this time. But let us walk, and you will tell me what you have come up with. Speak to me of these new thoughts.

Phil. So I shall. And I shall leave God out of our discussion. If He is, as you say, where thought begins and where it ends, we will allow Him on all sides of what we think and not confine Him within some category of thought. Agreed?

Hyl. Agreed.

Phil. And, I speak not of something I "came up with," Hylas. What woke me just before dawn was a series of events in science.

Hyl. How could that be! Science is based on a firm belief in matter.

Phil. I don't think so. Most scientists—almost all of them—assume matter exists. I will grant you that. But the practice of science operates as well without matter as with it. In fact, I hope to show that science is far better off without it.

Hyl. I am intrigued. What are these events of which you speak?

Phil. Do you know of Relativity Theory and Quantum Mechanics?

Hyl. I have heard of them, surely, though it has not been my purpose to understand them. Please do not take advantage of my ignorance.

Phil. I will not. My own understanding is limited as well, as I am not a physicist.

Hyl. Physics is too important to be left to the physicists.

Phil. Absolutely. Thank you, Hylas. You speak well; I could not have said it better myself. If there is civilian control of the military there should be civilian oversight of physics. We pay the professionals to play with the machines, but we must look over their shoulders.

Hyl. They don't like that, you know.

Phil. Yes, with good reason. We get in the way. But they need us.

Hyl. How do you mean?

Phil. Most scientists think they are working entirely without metaphysics. They think they are studying the world itself, "as it really is," without any sort of philosophy, theology, or other belief system. They consider their findings to be concrete, objective, and independent of opinion, prejudice, or preconceived notion.

Hyl. Is this not the case?

Phil. It is, for the most part. But in the last century science began to undermine its own metaphysical foundation, a foundation it did not know it had.

Hyl. I can think of no instance of a scientist referring to a metaphysical foundation for his or her work.

Phil. My point exactly: the metaphysical foundation I refer to is not a conscious choice. It is so deep an assumption that most are unaware of it.

Hyl. Are you speaking again of material substance?

Phil. I am. Scientists pride themselves in their skepticism, claiming to believe only that which can be proven to exist. This makes them impatient with metaphysical speculation. Yet they believe matter exists, without ever perceiving it. They do not see that matter is a belief, a faith, a metaphysical given that is accepted without the slightest proof. No one has ever, or will ever, experience anything beyond experience! It is the scientists themselves who are the metaphysicians! They believe in an unseen reality! They don't like philosophy because it opens their work to a subjective world they consider themselves to have transcended. They should realize the material world they are studying is founded on an unproven belief.

Hyl. I follow you. Scientists, and physicists in particular, are not as exempt from metaphysics as they may think. But what difference does this make? Matter or no matter, their work goes on. Right?

Phil. Right. This is the point I mentioned earlier. Science proceeds either way. The concept of matter is not necessary for doing science. More importantly, the concept of matter has begun to interfere with the progress of science.

Hyl. How is that?

Phil. I spoke of relativity theory. Without going into detail, let me mention a few things about it.

Hyl. Let us sit on the bench here in the shade.

Phil. Yes, a good idea. Relativity should be taken sitting down.

Hyl. I am not altogether ignorant of the subject, but speak to me of what you know and of how relativity disproves matter.

Phil. Relativity does not disprove matter. It merely stretches the concept of matter to a point where it is no longer useful.

Hyl. You have my attention, my friend. Go on.

Phil. The common sense view of the physical universe is something I call the "Box." In the Box material objects move about in space and time. Matter, space, and time all exist whether or not anyone is looking at them. They just are; maybe God created them, maybe He did not...

Hyl. I'm with you up to the God part.

Phil. OK. Sorry...

So, we have stars and galaxies, tables and chairs, and quarks and neutrinos all floating around in the Box obeying the laws of physics. "Consciousness" arises within some of these objects, most likely as an emergent complexity of physical process.

Hyl. All this sounds familiar. Then, along came relativity...

Phil. Space, time, and matter were all considered absolutes. There was nothing else more fundamental, nothing else they were made of, nothing else they depended on. They were the world itself.

Hyl. Then Einstein said time slows down for objects traveling near the speed of light.

Phil. Right. That's when I woke with a start. Time slows down at high velocities. And it's not only time: space shortens in the direction of motion, and worse yet, mass increases! Mass is supposed to be a measure of material content. How can matter magically increase as an object approaches the speed of light? Is more substance pumped into an object as it goes faster and faster? This is an absurdity.

Hyl. Yes. I admit these things are disturbing. I'm not sure how they can happen, but they do happen, it seems. That is just what is. But I don't see them happening here in the garden. The little stone I kicked a while ago did not slow down in time, shrink in the direction of its motion, or gain mass as far as I could tell. I know, according to Einstein, these dilations in space, time, and mass did, in fact, occur; but they were so small as to be immeasureable and certainly unnoticeable. They don't disturb my world-view—I did not lose any sleep over them—they happen in such extreme conditions that I do not have to think about them in my daily life.

Phil. But they clearly indicate that space, time, and mass are not absolute. There is something more fundamental.

Hyl. Perhaps. Or, the dilations are mere exceptions to the general rule.

Phil. They are not exceptions. You just admitted that the rock actually did shrink, slow down, and increase in mass, however slightly. This means that the entire universe, the "Box," exists in a more fundamental context, despite our assumptions to the contrary. With relativity, we began seeing around the corners of the Box. The universe we see is no longer in the Box; it is embedded in a wider reality. Relativity is not an exception to the rule; it is a new rule entirely.

Hyl. I, for one, can live with the universe I have always known. I need no new rules.

Phil. It gets worse, Hylas. What we thought were fixed structures of the physical world—space, time, and mass—are not fixed. They shrink and expand in ways that have something to do with the speed of light. There is some structural relation between light and dimensions, and that relation has something to do with consciousness. Einstein spoke of "observers" in "reference frames" moving at high speeds in relation to one another or, in other words, about consciousness. Suddenly, the "role of the observer" comes into physical science. Suddenly, we are no longer talking about an empty box; we are talking about what people experience.

Hyl. True, and "the role of the observer," I have heard, comes into play with quantum mechanics as well.

Phil. It does, as do space, time, mass, and light. There's a common thread running through both branches of physics—several common threads, in fact.

Hyl. Worth noticing, I admit.

Phil. Then there is $E = mc^2$. This famous equation shows the equivalence between mass and energy—everybody knows that. But look at the c^2—the speed of light again! What do mass and energy have to do with the speed of light, much less with the *square* of the speed of light? What is so special about light?

Hyl. You got me there, Philonous. I'm just as blown away by this as the next fellow. I'm glad we're sitting down.

Phil. It's all very mind-boggling, and one is tempted to throw one's hands in the air and walk away. But I think we can see something behind all this if we are able to see past the concept of matter.

Hyl. How is that? I recognize there is a pattern with space, time, and mass, and with the role of the observer, but how does matter (or non-matter) fit into your understanding?

Phil. First, we must look at what we mean by mass, then look at what we mean by dimension, and then re-evaluate the relation between dimensions and consciousness.

Hyl. A tall order, Philonous. The sun is climbing in the sky, and there are worldly concerns to distract us, but the plot thickens and I am intrigued. Speak on, my friend, and I will listen! The cares of the day can wait.

Phil. What I say sounds complicated but it is simple. I speak of everyday things: mass, dimensions, and consciousness, things you experience regularly, at this very moment, in fact. You already know what all of these things are. Looking at them in a new way may seem to complicate things, but bear with me if you will. Take mass, for instance. As I mentioned earlier, we have always thought of mass as a measure of material substance. I think, however, that we can better understand it as a dimension.

Hyl. A dimension? Really? Are we in mass, the way we are in space and time?

Phil. No. Not the same way. But I don't believe we are in space and time, either. More of that later when we talk about the relation between consciousness and dimensions.

Hyl. As you say. But I want to get back to that question. I want to be able to envision mass as a dimension.

Phil. We will get there. First, how do you experience mass?

Hyl. I feel it. And I think of it as the same thing as matter.

Phil. You feel it. Good, that is important. But how do you measure it?

Hyl. With a scale. It weighs, right?

Phil. It weighs if you are in a gravitational field.

Hyl. We are, are we not?

Phil. Yes, but if we happened to be in interstellar space, how would you measure mass? There would be no gravitating bodies around to pull it this way or that.

Hyl. I would measure mass by its resistance to acceleration. The more massive an object, the slower it accelerates when subject to a given force.

Phil. Right! We measure mass by resistance to acceleration. But by what terms do we measure acceleration?

Hyl. We measure acceleration in terms of meters per second per second.

Phil. Right again, Hylas! You know your physics, my friend. Acceleration, by which we measure mass, is expressed in terms of meters per second per second. Acceleration is a change in velocity: a slowing down or a speeding up, even a change in the direction of velocity. Going around a curve or over a bump is a form of acceleration. That's where the "per second per second" comes in. Uniform velocity (without acceleration) is measured in simpler terms of meters per second (or miles per hour) without the other per second. So, to measure acceleration we need another time dimension! I suggest this second time dimension is, in fact, the mass dimension.

Hyl. Whoa. That's a long chain of logic—with a bit of a leap at the end. But go on...

Phil. Once mass becomes a dimension we no longer need matter to do science.

Hyl. In eliminating matter you have created a whole new dimension of physical reality. You have traded one assumption for another.

Phil. I created nothing. I simply noticed that mass acts as a dimension, much as do space and time. Mass has always been there. We measure momentum, energy, power, pressure, force, etc., in terms of space, time, and mass, and often interchange these dimensional values when calculating interactions among physical objects. In relativity theory, it is space, time, and mass that are distorted near the speed of light. In the vicinity of massive bodies, four-dimensional space-time is curved into the mass dimension.

Hyl. Did Einstein say that, too?

Phil. Not exactly. I'm thinking as I go, Hylas. Have patience.

Hyl. But objects are not in mass the way they are in space and time.

Phil. True. We do not experience mass as immediately as space or time. We "see" it only as a second time dimension. But here's something else. We feel mass but we do not feel velocity. There is a clear distinction between the two. You could be whizzing by at a million miles per hour and feel not a thing. But if you were to change your velocity—even slightly—you would feel it. This is the difference between one time dimension and two.

Hyl. I feel velocity every time I ride in a car, even when not accelerating. I feel the road beneath the wheels.

Phil. Actually, you don't feel velocity. What you feel are the bumps and curves—the accelerations, however slight they may be. These are little dips into the mass dimension. If you were to travel in a straight line on a perfectly smooth highway, you would not know you were traveling at all until you looked out the window.

Hyl. Yes, I recall that now. You are indeed correct, my friend.

Phil. The difference between velocity and acceleration is not merely a measurement. It is a structural foundation of the physical universe.

Hyl. If you say so. Can you help me now to envision this fifth dimension?

Phil. I will try, but it may not work. What do you feel right now?

Hyl. The ground beneath my feet, the breeze upon my face, a hand on my hip: I'm certainly not accelerating anywhere.

Phil. The gravity you feel under your feet—and throughout your body—is a form of acceleration, the same sort of full-body acceleration you feel in an airplane gathering speed along the runway. This is the mass dimension as a whole. The breeze on your face and the hand on your hip are partial accelerations that are balanced elsewhere in your body. In this sense, you are "in" the mass dimension. It is what you feel.

Hyl. I can see what you are saying if I try hard enough, but it seems forced.

Phil. Admittedly, we are not really "in" mass, or in space-time. We are re-examining the relation between dimensions and consciousness. The "Box" assumes consciousness is inside space and time (inside living objects that are themselves inside space and time). The big revolution here is to switch them around—put the dimensions, including mass, inside consciousness!

Hyl. Oh my. I'm glad we are still sitting. Everything you say is revolutionary. This last bit only piles it on deeper.

Phil. This last bit is the great leap from one way of looking at reality to another. All else follows.

Hyl. Then why did you not say so initially?

Phil. Perhaps I should have. It's hard to know where to start. I'm sure you appreciate that these ideas are as disturbing to me as to anyone.

Hyl. Yes, well, let us rise and walk a while. I need a stirring of the blood. But please, go on, if there is more.

Phil. Unfortunately, there is. I have not yet tried to explain what a dimension is.

Hyl. Yes, you promised to address that.

Phil. Before that, there is another subject we must address: quantum mechanics.

Hyl. I nearly forgot. Perhaps we should find a place to sit for that one.

Phil. I shall keep walking if it is the same to you. But please, know I am just now working these things out. They have been rattling loosely in my mind since the pre-dawn hours, and I have not yet fully assembled them into a logical sequence.

Hyl. I understand, even if I do not understand. So how does quantum mechanics fit in here? Are we talking the Heisenberg Uncertainty Principle? Probability? Observer-created reality? Quantum weirdness?

Phil. All of the above, but again, only the broad picture. Let us stick to Heisenberg.

Hyl. Of course.

Phil. What do you remember of the Uncertainty Principle?

Hyl. It has something to do with not being able to know where a particle is in space-time.

Phil. Actually, in space-time-mass.

Hyl. Oh.

Phil. Heisenberg discovered that at extremely small dimensions it is impossible to know a particle's location in space and time and its momentum (velocity times mass) at the same time. The more you know about where a particle is, the less you can possibly know about its motion (momentum); and the more you know about its motion, the less you can possibly know about its location.

Hyl. That's not so surprising at such small dimensions. It's hard to get good readings when you're talking about billionths of a centimeter.

Phil. But the Heisenberg principle has nothing to do with limits in instrumentation. Even with perfect microscopes and perfect particle detectors there is an absolute limit to what we can know about objects in space, time, and mass. It is physically impossible to know more. This is a limit built into the universe.

Hyl. Oh, you mean objects can only be so small and no smaller?

Phil. Not exactly. What this means is you reach a point at extremely small dimensions where space, time, and mass begin to merge. They are no longer distinct from one another. You can still detect things at smaller and smaller space dimensions, but if you do, the time of your observations becomes unsure, and you can no longer say what part of a particle's momentum is mass and what part velocity (space divided by time.) Physicists speak of space-time as a sort of "fabric" that unravels if you look too closely. Seeing a particle at quantum dimensions is like looking too closely at a newspaper photograph.

Hyl. You mean where you can see the little ink dots?

Phil. Yes. From a distance you can make out objects in a newspaper photo: faces, cars, buildings, etc., but up close you see dots and spaces between the dots. Your mind connects the dots into a pattern. Physical reality is itself discontinuous, only the "dots" are so small nobody noticed them until Planck discovered the quantum.

Hyl. What is a quantum?

Phil. It's a tiny piece of energy. Everybody assumed, including Planck, that energy was perfectly smooth and continuous, and that you could divide it infinitely into smaller and smaller parts. Planck discovered that energy comes in little indivisible packets he named quanta—the tiny dots that come together in our minds as physical objects.

Hyl. He didn't say that, did he?

Phil. No. Sorry, I'm rambling again. But Planck showed that energy and space-time are quantized, or discontinuous. A tiny particle "leaps" from one quantum to another, without passing through space between quanta. In fact, there is no space between quanta, even though they are not "touching" each other. Space-time-mass disintegrates on the quantum level, and it is this disintegration that shows up as the Uncertainty Principle.

119

Hyl. So, like relativity theory, quantum mechanics deals with limits to the dimensional universe.

Phil. Yes.

Hyl. I have read that it also involves the role of the observer.

Phil. Yes. We can no longer properly speak of a physical event happening in isolation from the act of observation. Consciousness is always involved when a measurement is made.

Hyl. Both relativity and quantum mechanics, though they are separate branches of physical science, also involve the strange properties of light. Light is shown to have a dual nature, behaving at times like a wave and at other times like a stream of particles. It can be either one or the other, but not both at the same time.

Phil. Yes, exactly. You have that right. Light again! Light has momentum, but no mass. This is impossible in normal reality, of course, because momentum is defined as mass times velocity.

Hyl. What is it about light? How can it have momentum without mass? Why is it so strange? I think of it as tiny particles—photons—hurtling through space and bouncing off walls and things, but that's not really it, is it?

Phil. That view works for a while but falls apart if you look too closely.

Hyl. How so?

Phil. There is a circularity in our understanding of light, which, when realized, might point us in a better direction. The circularity is that a line in space is defined as the line taken by a ray of light.

Hyl. Yes. I am familiar with that definition. It works even in curved space-time, does it not?

120

Phil. Yes, it does. But if you define space in terms of light, how can you define light in terms of space?

Hyl. What do you mean?

Phil. If space is determined by how light moves, how can you say anything about light in terms of space?

Hyl. I don't know. How do you?

Phil. You don't. You don't try to find light in space. You look for space in light.

Hyl. Aaaah…

Phil. This is the paradigm shift! This puts dimensions within consciousness instead of consciousness within dimensions. Light is not a particle or a wave in space; light is visual consciousness itself! "c," the so-called "velocity" of light, is really the relation of space and time in perceptual consciousness. There are "c" meters of space in a second of time. Looking across the room or across the universe, we are looking one second back in time for every "c" meters of space.

Hyl. Whoa. You're going a little too fast here.

Phil. Physicists since the days of Michelson and Morley have been looking for light in space, and it's just not there!

Hyl. That is a weighty shift. I will have to chew on that one for a while. I wonder if this has to do with the constancy of the speed of light and the speed of light as an upper limit of any velocity?

Phil. Why yes, I suppose it does. But now you're going too fast for me.

Hyl. An accomplishment on my part. I didn't think I could do that.

Phil. It would seem both our minds are racing. It is exhausting, however exhilarating. Here, let us sit again. I must catch my breath. There is shade by the tree.

Hyl. We are nearly round the garden and the sun is high overhead. But there are some points I would have you clear before we complete the circuit. I shall postpone the midday meal, if that is agreeable to you.

Phil. Yes, let us pull some things together before we leave the discussion. I can hardly think of eating just yet.

Hyl. You were going to give me a new understanding of just what a dimension is.

Phil. Yes, I have been thinking about this. But it is purely speculative, you understand.

Hyl. Of course.

Phil. For the "Box," you will remember, a dimension, whether of space or of time, is a fundamental structure of the external physical world. It has nothing to do with consciousness. I think our understanding of the physical world works better, considering the discoveries of relativity theory and quantum mechanics, if we understand a dimension to be a fundamental structure of consciousness.

Hyl. Yes, you have said this much, but I would have you spell it out further.

Phil. So I shall. Let us speak, then, of information.

Hyl. Information? You continually surprise me.

Phil. Information is a pattern that could be some other pattern: a pattern of letters, colors, objects, sounds, pixels, etc., that might have been something else. When you hear that the Dodgers scored three runs in the bottom of the fifth inning, it is information because they could have scored two, or twenty, or none. When a telegraph key strikes a dot and three dashes instead of some other combination, it is a "J," and not a "Y" or a "B." When a page of Shakespeare appears on your computer screen, the shapes of the letters and blank spaces between them could have been something else: a picture of the Eiffel Tower, perhaps.

Hyl. Yes....

Phil. Each information system is a range of possibilities, or a potential, within which the actual is located. Only some of the possibilities are realized. The Dodgers could have scored zero to infinity runs; each dot could have been a dash and each dash a dot; and each black pixel on your computer screen could have been white, or some other color. The meaning of the information you receive is as much in the potential as in the actual.

Hyl. Yes, I'm with you so far. And dimensions are...?

Phil. Dimensions are sensory potentials. The information within each of our senses is arranged at a location within a dimensional potential. How many dimensions have we discussed?

Hyl. Three of space, and two of time, the second time dimension being that of mass.

Phil. Five, then, correct?

Hyl. Yes.

Phil. And how many realms of sensory perception have we?

Hyl. Five.

Phil. The mass dimension is associated with what we feel.

Hyl. Yes, in the form of acceleration. And light, you are about to remind me, is the visual realm of consciousness.

Phil. You are quick, Hylas.

Hyl. The number five could be coincidental. I am unconvinced. Also, what I hear or taste has nothing to do with where I see it in space or time.

Phil. True. But what you hear or taste are actual perceptions, not potential. It is the information potentials—not the actuals—that are coordinated into the dimensional universe we experience in everyday life. You must understand a physical object as a range of points in space-time-mass. Where and when you see that range of points is where and when you potentially hear, taste, smell, or touch it. You actually touch very little of what you see; but you know if you were to reach out in the direction of a visual image, you would experience a tactile image at that location.

Hyl. Yes. I see what you are saying. And it is this coordination of sensory potentials into space-time that creates the illusion of independent existence: of material substance. When we see an object in space we think of it sitting there, waiting for us to touch or taste it.

Phil. Exactly.

Hyl. You have browbeaten me again, Philonous.

Phil. No, I hope not. You have said much of this with your own words.

Hyl. Yes, I admit. However, I must reconsider much of what I have said. I fear I have merely anticipated your words. But tell me something else. The dimensional structure you have described here is an alternative explanation for the physical world we experience in everyday life. What does this have to do with relativity and quantum mechanics?

Phil. We must speak of light one last time.

Hyl. If you say so.

Phil. You will remember that a cornerstone of modern physics is the dual nature of light.

Hyl. Light is either particle or wave, but never both.

Phil. One of the early quantum discoveries was Einstein's photoelectric effect, which shows that photons, as tiny particles, can knock electrons out of the atoms of certain metallic elements. Though they have no mass, photons have momentum—they can push things around. You could actually feel them.

Hyl. But you have defined light as visual consciousness, not tactile.

Phil. This is my point. On the everyday scale of things, light is visual. At around the quantum level light is both tactile and visual, but not distinctly either.

Hyl. Aha: the dual nature! But these are two separate realms of perception. Which dimensional potential will they appear in?

Phil. Neither. And both. The potentials fall apart where visual consciousness becomes tactile. Space-time breaks down at precisely the level at which light is neither distinctly wave nor particle. We cannot say where something is, or what it is doing at that level. Where sensory realms disintegrate is exactly where dimensions disintegrate. This indicates their essential identity. The relation of space to time is derived from light.

Hyl. By the mathematical relation "c," no doubt.

Phil. True.

Hyl. And the relation of mass to space-time by the relation "c^2."

Phil. Yes!... from Einstein's equation!

Hyl. Yes! So, this is why space-time is in light, and not light in space-time.

Phil. And why nothing can travel faster than light, as you mentioned earlier.

Hyl. I thought there might be a connection. We cannot see velocity faster than "c" in a space-time built with only "c" meters for every second.

Phil. Yes. You are getting ahead of me, Hylas, and that is good. I believe we will find more connections the more we look. When we first pull things apart everything seems confounded and unrelated, but we are finding connections that put the pieces together again.

Hyl. I should hope so. I would be hard pressed to remember all the strands we have unraveled this morning. And I hope we can tie a few more together before we part. I do not as yet see a clear picture of the whole, though I am developing some faith that there might be one.

Phil. Let us rise, then, and complete the circuit of this wonderful garden. As we walk I will attempt to present you with a new model of perceptual consciousness that will re-weave some loose strands. I am still working on it, of course, so please bear with me.

Hyl. Let us walk slowly then, for I would hear you out. But wait... I have thought of another connection. c^2 is a four-dimensional constant, am I right?"

Phil. Yes. Meters squared per second squared.

Hyl. And are not four dimensions of space-time created when the "touch" of a photon becomes visual consciousness?

Phil. Interesting, Hylas! Now you are way ahead of me! I would have to mull that one over…

Hyl. I am by no means sure of it. But to get back: you were weaving loose strands into a new model of perceptual consciousness?

Phil. I will try to replace the "Box" with what I call the "Screen."

Hyl. As in TV or computer screen?

Phil. Precisely.

Hyl. That is something I can envision.

Phil. Can you envision a three-dimensional screen?

Hyl. Something like a holograph, I suppose.

Phil. Yes. The screen is actually four-dimensional, as it includes time.

Hyl. But not mass?

Phil. Mass is foreshortened on the screen. It is crammed into the time dimension, much the way a three-dimensional object is crammed into two dimensions in a picture or photograph. We don't see mass directly, but we know it is there by the way objects move in space-time.

Hyl. And we feel it under acceleration.

Phil. Yes! And even without acceleration we actually "feel" the individual photons of which the screen is constructed.

Hyl. I don't feel photons.

Phil. No, you don't, but you sense them in the form of color. The impact of each photon is experienced as a frequency, or color. This is what turns tactile consciousness into visual. Color is our experience of the mass dimension in the form of visual consciousness. We do not experience the mass of objects themselves in this manner; we experience only the photons of which the screen is constructed. Do you know, by the way, the dimensional units of frequency?

Hyl. Uuuuh... It would have to be time, or seconds... No, it would be per second.

Phil. Bingo.

Hyl. Mass? You just rewove a loose strand.

Phil. I hope so. I think this is right.

Hyl. So physical reality is like watching 3D television. But we are not that detached. Why do we feel like our bodies are on (or in) the screen?

Phil. The dimensional potentials are not fixed. The axes of space-time-mass can be rotated. Uniform velocity is a rotation of space into time: it seems as though we are moving through space as space scrolls past us in the opposite direction. This gives us the sense of being in space. Acceleration is a rotation of space-time into the mass dimension: velocity changes in rate or direction as we feel the entire body.

Hyl. So it only seems we are in space and time?

Phil. Space and time coordinate our perceptual experience. They are fundamental structures of consciousness.

Hyl. Oh. We cannot say, then, that the screen itself is anywhere or "anywhen." Am I right?

Phil. Yes, Hylas.

Hyl. But can you say anything about what constitutes the screen?

Phil. Yes, I can. The screen is composed of quanta—those tiny little packets of energy that Planck discovered. Photons are a form of quanta. They are extremely small, but not infinitely small, so the screen is not perfectly continuous. It is grainy, like the newspaper photo we talked about earlier. What you actually see on the screen are patterns of dots your mind puts together into a picture.

Hyl. Aha! Allow me to anticipate you once again. Physical objects are no more than patterns of quanta on the screen, so there is no need to suppose there is substance behind them—no need for matter, right? Tables and chairs are just shadows.

Phil. Shadows that we can touch…

Hyl. This is the strand we began with, if I remember back that far.

Phil. Yes, it is. We have gone through a lot of trouble to get rid of matter. But if it was never there, we did not really get rid of it, did we?

Hyl. I certainly thought it was there. I slept well thinking it was safe, and now I can no longer say much either way. But tell me, Philonous: the sun is now lower in the sky, we have completed our walk in the garden, and you have tied nearly everything into a tidy picture of physical reality, but I still have a question: a big one.

Phil. Yes. I would be disappointed if you had not.

Hyl. Whose screen is this? Whose consciousness? Yours or mine? Or someone else's? Please don't tell me it is God's. And no rhetorical tricks, either—I have bought too much already today.

Phil. I could not do justice to your question were we to stand here until the sun fell entirely below the horizon. But I have thought on this long and hard. It is an extremely important part of the overall picture—the most important part, in fact—and I will say what I can while we are standing here.

Hyl. This also gets back to the existence of matter, as it is not only the coordination of sensory experience that produces the "illusion" of matter, as you call it...

Phil. I did not call it an illusion. You did. Immaterialism does not imply that the world is illusory, or that "nothing really exists;" it implies that what appears to be independent existence is more parsimoniously understood to be a structure of perceptual consciousness.

Hyl. All right. Whatever. But the independent existence of matter is confirmed, seemingly, when you tell me you see something that I see. There has to be something "out there" making both of us see the same thing at the same time. This path that we have just walked on, do you not see it?

Phil. Yes, I do, Hylas. But here is the key. You see the path and you hear me say I see it, but you do not experience me seeing it. Your actual experience is limited to the vision of the path and the sound of my voice arranged into words.

Hyl. What? Are you saying you do not exist? You are no more than a machine that repeats my sensory experience back to me? Or do you suppose that I do not exist, and this screen you speak of is a figment of your imagination?

Phil. No, not at all. But you are on to something here. Direct perceptual experience appears to be physically equivalent to communication among observers, but it is not. Much of what we know of the world is what has been told us, and not what we perceive directly. These are two separate types of experience in entirely separate realms of consciousness. If I say there is a blackbird sitting on a branch behind you, you would likely accept my words as equivalent to seeing the blackbird yourself, but the words and the visual image are entirely distinct.

Hyl. Allow me to experiment. I hear you tell me of the bird, and now... I turn and see the bird in the tree, where you said it would be. These are distinct experiences, in separate realms of consciousness, as you say. But they are of the same thing. You say bird; I see bird. I know through the sound of your words that the bird is there before I see it myself. How does this disprove the existence of a material bird sitting in a tree all the while?

Phil. The observational realm of consciousness, within which the sound of my words becomes information, is dimensionally coordinated with the five perceptual realms in the same manner as they are coordinated with each other. You see the blackbird where and when I say I see it.

Hyl. Just what do you mean by this observational realm?

Phil. I mean information from observers as opposed to direct perceptual experience.

Hyl. Why is not what I hear you say in the auditory realm?

Phil. The sound is, of course, auditory. But the order of the sound—the words—turns a purely auditory experience into information that you experience in the observational realm. You hear the sound of my words, but at the same time, through their order, you become aware of a blackbird at a location in the tree—a blackbird you are not seeing, hearing, tasting, or smelling, or touching.

Hyl. And this dimensional coordination is supposed to explain why I hear you say you see the same thing I see directly?

Phil. You are exactly right.

Hyl. Well, perhaps, but this business of dimensionally-coordinated realms of consciousness is entirely new to me, and I would think, to anyone else.

Phil. Has it occurred to you that we, in the Western tradition, do not know much about consciousness? We are good at science and technology, but we push aside questions about conscious experience. We think of it as too mysterious to be worthy of consideration. Have you not noticed this?

Hyl. It is true, I admit.

Phil. There are other traditions that make a disciplined study of consciousness. We cannot discuss the content of these traditions as we stand here in the afternoon sun, but I would suggest that their approach may be helpful in appreciating what modern physics has discovered. I believe we are forced to accept consciousness as a first principle. Also, we will come to realize consciousness is not the same as self.

Hyl. How would this apply to my question?

Phil. The difference between seeing the path and hearing me say I see it, is a difference between the visual and observational realms of consciousness. It is not a difference between two separate consciousnesses—not a difference between you and me.

Hyl. But, Philonous, this seems a gratuitous construction. You are in need of another explanation, so you invent another "realm" of consciousness.

Phil. I admit it seems artificial. But again, Hylas, I think I have noticed it, not invented it. It is not just another realm; it is a realm dimensionally coordinated with perceptual consciousness. Observational consciousness is not just any sound that comes out of my mouth; it is only sound crafted into symbols that coordinate in space and time with perceptual consciousness.

Hyl. Can you give an example?

Phil. Suppose I were to say: "There is an elephant standing on the path behind you," or "I see a leprechaun sitting on your shoulder," or "Blaaaaaa!" None of this would be observational consciousness because I'm not speaking of anything I actually see. However, if I say, "There is a blackbird nine feet directly behind you and twelve feet off the ground," what I say coordinates in space and time with what I experience in the visual realm. It is, therefore, observational. Observational information is always potential perception—you can always look for yourself and see what I say I am seeing.

Hyl. And might there be a dimensional potential associated with this realm, as there are with the five perceptual realms?

Phil. There is.

Hyl. Really! Do tell.

Phil. Do you remember how careful we were to distinguish between acceleration and velocity?

Hyl. Yes. Acceleration, or non-uniform velocity, requires two dimensions of time, while uniform velocity requires only one.

Phil. Precisely. There is also a distinction between uniform and non-uniform acceleration; each coordinates with a separate dimension

Hyl. Would we ever notice the distinction?

Phil. All the time. Do you remember how the mass dimension is foreshortened in space-time?

Hyl. The fifth dimension is crammed into the four dimensional "screen" of perceptual consciousness. Is observational consciousness another such foreshortening?

Phil. It is. Mass is revealed through uniform acceleration in space-time, observation through non-uniform acceleration.

Hyl. Help me to envision this.

Phil. It's actually quite easy. Observers are alive, right? What distinguishes their motion from that of inanimate objects?

Hyl. They move around things they see. They react to the environment. They have purpose in their motion.

Phil. They change their acceleration. The dimensional potential for observational consciousness is non-uniform acceleration. This is a dimension larger than space-time-mass. Actual information within this potential is order. Observers create order. This is what makes them look alive.

Hyl. And, to anticipate your next sentence, the words you use to describe the blackbird and its location are orderly.

Phil. Yes. In the same way you detect a potential for tactile perception through the five-dimensional behavior of inanimate objects, you detect the potential for observational information through the six-dimensional behavior of animate objects.

Hyl. Do you mean by this that there is no consciousness in observers: only orderly motion?

Phil. Consciousness is not in observers any more than mass is in objects. But I do not mean that observers are not conscious. I mean that there is no separate consciousness in observers. In the same sense that there is no independently existing matter in physical objects, there is no independently existing consciousness in observers. The same structure of consciousness explains the apparent existence of both.

Hyl. So, there is no difference between you and me?

Phil. Yes. There is a difference. It is a difference in the level of consciousness and not a difference between "two consciousnesses." We are separate selves, each creating our own order in the world, but there is only one consciousness.

Hyl. What a thought! What do you mean by level of consciousness?

Phil. I mean the difference between perceptual and observational consciousness. Perceptual consciousness exists on the level of the individual in the form of five sensory realms. It is possible to experience only perception, as, for instance, if you listened to the sound of my words without paying attention to their meaning, or if you heard a foreign language. Observational consciousness is a higher level that arises over and above perception. It is not "in you" or "in me."

Hyl. So, perceptual consciousness is "you and I," where observational consciousness is "both of us."

Phil. Almost, but not exactly. Perceptual consciousness might be better expressed as "you *or* I." But truly, consciousness, whether perceptual or observational, is not one of us; nor is it both of us. It is the direct experience of seeing, hearing, thinking, observing, etc. It is a single picture artificially divided by self.

Hyl. Now there's a mindful. And the observational realm is a world larger than either of us could experience perceptually?

Phil. A full dimension larger. Think of all we know of the world through other people, through newspapers, telephones, televisions, computers, the Internet…

Hyl. And only recently. A generation or two back, most experience was perceptual. We saw the world directly, with the occasional shout from the next room.

Phil. The difference is science. Here's a definition for you, Hylas: "Science is a systematic construction of the observational realm of consciousness."

Hyl. Explain please.

Phil. I defined observation earlier as potential perception.

Hyl. I remember.

Phil. A scientific fact is one that can be perceived by any observer at any time under the same conditions, or in other words, a scientific fact is potential perception. Scientists continually test and re-test what they say they see to be sure it can be seen by anyone. This is the scientific method. This is the systematic creation of observational consciousness.

Hyl. But it is only one realm of consciousness among many.

Phil. Exactly. Science is a special construction of conscious experience. The scientific method systematically excludes other dimensional realms (perceptual consciousness) and all non-dimensional consciousness (thought, dream, opinion, imagination, spiritual experience, etc.). Science is not all of consciousness and not all of reality.

Hyl. ...Ahhh. So, in other words, you are saying science remains surrounded by a larger reality that includes perception and what you call non-dimensional consciousness.

Phil. Science is embedded in a larger reality.

Hyl. So, when I think about an old friend or I dream about flying to the moon, these experiences are real, but they are not science.

Phil. True. This has an important consequence.

Hyl. What might that be?

Phil. Because science is part of consciousness, and not consciousness of science, there will never be a scientific understanding of consciousness.

Hyl. Oh my! What a shame. I have often hoped that we would one day have such an understanding. But... what about recent research in brain physiology? We know so much more now about which particular neural processes take place in various parts of the brain.

Phil. We do. This is, as you say, neural process. It is not conscious experience. We will never locate consciousness in the brain.

Hyl. You may be wrong in this.

Phil. I will risk it. You understand, Hylas, that though science is not the world itself, it remains our greatest resource in understanding the physical world.

Hyl. Physical, then, is not the same as material.

Phil. It is not. Remove material substance, and the physical world remains.

Hyl. Yet you are saying that the myth of material substance underlies the scientific tradition, as if we in the West took a wrong turn several hundred years ago. Is the East fundamentally right, and the West wrong?

Phil. No, no, not at all! True, the concept of matter operates much like a mythology, but it is a mythology that has served well for a long time. The West has led the world in the last half millennium with the help of this mythology. Only in the last hundred years has science outgrown it. If we wish to progress in the future— and I daresay we do—we must re-examine this fundamental metaphysical assumption.

Hyl. I am glad to see, Philonous, you do not reject the accomplishments of the scientific tradition. I would have to add that through electronic technology, it is science, or the observational realm, as you would call it, which is evolving most rapidly in the present day.

Phil. It is. Once relieved of the "material" world, we see life moving forward in a much larger universe. Human beings become more than bodies bouncing about in space-time. We become a new sentience, a higher echelon of life, an emerging wholeness over and above the individual level.

Hyl. All this from relativity theory and quantum mechanics?

Phil. Yes, I think so.

Hyl. It seems you have built an entire new world from a handful of physical curiosities.

Phil. Perhaps. But remember, it was a few curiosities in planetary motion that created the heliocentric universe.

Hyl. True.

Phil. We tend, at first, to concentrate on little ways in which the old understanding no longer serves: through relativity theory we glimpse around the corners of the Box, through quantum mechanics we see clear through it. We develop a larger context within which we see the limitations of the old understanding. When there is a clear vision of the Box as a whole, we see that we are not in it. This is the leap from the old to the new: a radical change in where we are looking from, and therefore, in who we understand ourselves to be.

Hyl. I am staggered. My brain is full to overflowing, and I am most grateful for your patience with me today.

Phil. I daresay you were the patient one.

Hyl. We have labored on these thoughts together, each in our way. But tell me, Philonous, why is it, do you think, we have had such an extended discussion today after it seemed we had exhausted the conversation in our previous encounters?

Phil. Our original author had not the benefit of twentieth century physics.

Hyl. He had the original insight, however.

Phil. He did. He saw a truth that took him only so far in his own time. Were he here now, I daresay he would have had much more to say.

Hyl. His spirit lives on, Philonous, in you and in me. Perhaps we shall meet again one day soon.

Phil. Perhaps. But we have exhausted this author, Hylas, and will need another, I am certain.

Hyl. I bid you good day, Philonous.

Phil. And good day to you, my friend.

PHYSICS & NEAR-DEATH EXPERIENCE

*Presentation to the International Association for
Near-Death Studies, Boston*

August 1, 2015

I am interested in the relation of consciousness to physics.

Not many years ago most people, particularly physicists, would have said that there is no relation between consciousness and physics: you can have all the physics you want without any consciousness at all. But that is changing fast. Now, it is generally accepted that physics cannot exist without consciousness. There is no general acceptance of what this means, but there is a general acceptance that it means something.

Let me begin with a conclusion: I have found that to understand modern physics, it is absolutely essential to distinguish between self and consciousness. Those of us in the Western tradition tend to think of self and consciousness as the same thing. But they are not. *Self* is one thing, and *consciousness* is something else. They are not entirely separate, but neither are they the same. That is the main thing I have to say.

The separation of self and consciousness has great consequence for the meaning of near-death experience, and for the meaning of death itself. I did not personally realize the distinction between self and consciousness through a near-death experience, or through study of philosophy or religion, or through some need to invent a construction that fits a theory or an opinion. I came to this understanding through a study of physics. If we are to understand the meaning of modern physics, self and consciousness cannot be the same thing.

I'm not a physicist. Not being a physicist is important to what I do. I go outside of physics and look back. Because I'm not a professional, I am able to glimpse things beyond space and time without getting into trouble with the authorities.

What does physics have to do with near-death experience? Nothing, really... physics is about this world, about what happens inside space and time. But my interest is not in the everyday workings of physics (the lab coats, the particle accelerators, and those squiggly things on the blackboard). I'm interested in what happens at the edges of the physical world: in the weird discoveries made in the last century in relativity theory and quantum mechanics. These strange findings, or *enigmas*, as I call them, appear to us within space and time—within physics—but indicate, in a very powerful and scientifically rigorous manner, that space and time are not the ultimate reality. This is the point of connection between physics and near-death experience.

Let me mention four enigmas of modern physics:

1. At extremely high velocities near the speed of light, space gets shorter, time slows down, and mass increases. If a space ship were flying by at 90% of the speed of light, all the objects inside would be less than half as long, clocks would be ticking half as fast, and everything would weigh twice as much. This is science fact, not science fiction; it has been experimentally proven many times over.

2. At extremely small dimensions, space, time, and mass blend into one another. You can't tell them apart. If you know where a subatomic particle such as an electron is, you cannot know its momentum (its velocity times mass). This is not due to inaccuracy of measurement; it is a limitation built into the fabric of the universe. Space and time are not infinitely divisible. As you cut them up into smaller and smaller pieces, they mix into each other, and into mass.

3. Near the extreme gravitational field of a black hole, space collapses and time comes to a standstill. If you and I were playing tag somewhere in outer space near a black hole, and I were to slip and fall, you would never see me fall in. I would see (and feel) myself falling through the event horizon, never to return, but you would not. As I got closer to the event horizon, you would see the passage of time becoming slower and slower, approaching zero at the horizon itself. You would never see me get that far. My image would gradually fade the closer I got to the edge of the hole.

Four: As you look out across the universe, you are looking back in time. When you look at the Andromeda Galaxy two million light years away, you are looking two million years back in time. Even as you look across the room, you are seeing the wall on the far side as it was a billionth of a second ago. Space is built from time.

These enigmas are rarely experienced directly (except for looking back in time), yet each of them has been scientifically proven many times. They are very real and very well known. They are not speculations. They are part of the physical world—this world.

The enigmas show that the physical world of space and time is not absolute. It is not the most fundamental reality. Space and time contain the objects of our seeing and hearing and touching, but they do not contain consciousness itself.

The physical world is the context of our everyday lives, but not the context of life itself.

The enigmas have three things in common: dimensional extremes, consciousness, and light. They all have to do with *dimensions*: space, time, and mass. Mass is traditionally understood to be a measure of material substance within an object. But I have found that mass works better as a dimension. Matter is an obsolete concept that gets in the way. (More on that in a minute...) All of the enigmas of modern physics involve conscious experience at dimensional extremes: extremes of distance, velocity, gravity, and size. They all involve what happens to perceptual consciousness at the far edges of the dimensional world. Because we normally inhabit the middle latitudes of space and time rather than the extremes, we are untroubled by these enigmas in our everyday lives.

All the enigmas involve the "role of the observer," or, in other words, what someone experiences. They are all about consciousness.

We can no longer speak of physical reality in the absence of conscious experience.

And the enigmas of modern physics all have to do with light. Light is not "out there," in space.

Light is visual consciousness.

Light is not in space; space is in light. All of the difficulties in understanding the nature of light stem from trying to see light in space.

The physical discoveries of the twentieth century are leading up to what is likely to become the paradigm shift of the twenty-first century. To understand what physical science has been trying to tell us for a hundred years, we will have to change our understanding of the relation between consciousness and dimensions. We have assumed, to the present day, that consciousness is *inside* space and time, but we will have to understand space and time inside consciousness. That's the paradigm shift. Consciousness is more fundamental than the physical world. In other words, the physical world is a subset of consciousness.

Try that on for size—right now.

"The physical world is a subset of consciousness."

As you sit there, you are aware of the room you are in, the time of day, the season, and the streets and buildings surrounding you. You likely think of consciousness inside the brain, inside the room. But try, for a moment, to think of the room inside consciousness. Think of light as visual consciousness. Think of everything you *perceive* in the room—all the tables and chairs—as *dimensional* experience. Think of other experience, things like imagination, thought, emotion, and spiritual experience as *non-dimensional*. Dimensional and non-dimensional experiences are equally real. Think of dimensional experience—the room—being *inside* the larger scope of consciousness as a whole. Perhaps you will catch a glimpse of this understanding as you sit now. Rather than thought being an approximation of physical reality, think of physical reality as a condensation of thought within the dimensions.

The physical world is not an illusion—I do not deny its reality—I simply understand it in a different way. I put the physical world inside the larger context of being alive. There is no logical way to make the transition to this point of view, or to argue for it. But once the transition is made, physics suddenly makes better sense.

That's it. That is the paradigm shift. That is what I have been working on for the last forty years. Consciousness is not in space and time; space and time are in consciousness.

There is no external universe independent of consciousness.

There are several huge questions that immediately follow this realization. Here are three of them:

1. What does this say about *material substance* existing independently of consciousness?

2. What does it say about the relation of "one" consciousness to "another"?

3. And what does it say about the meaning of death?

All of these questions follow from the paradigm shift, from taking consciousness out of the dimensions and putting the dimensions inside consciousness. There is a book or two within each of these questions—maybe a feature length film. I have time for only a few words for each.

The first question concerns the existence of material substance:

No one has ever experienced material substance. We all see things, touch things, hear things, etc., but all we really have are the seeing, touching, and hearing. For a long time people have said we have these perceptual experiences because some sort of material existence outside of consciousness *causes* them. They say *matter has to exist* in order to make sense of the world. But ultimately, you must admit there can be no direct proof for the existence of anything we do not actually experience—you can't experience anything outside of experience. I, in turn, will have to admit there is no proof for the *non-existence* of matter. I will never be able to prove it does not exist and I never intend to try.

But there is something I want to point out. ... What makes it *seem* like matter is there? What is it *specifically* about seeing, touching, and hearing a physical object that makes us think matter is "out there" independent of perception?

The answer is: *dimensions.* What we see, touch, and hear appears to be material because we perceive an object in each of the sensory realms at the same location in space and time. We reach out and touch what we see. We think, "Ah, there must be something out there *causing* me to see and touch something at the same place in space and time." The dimensions have something to do with how we put separate perceptions together into the experience of a physical object.

Again, I am not saying that physical objects don't exist—they do. I am saying they do not exist outside of perceptual consciousness; it is the *dimensional structure* of perceptual consciousness that makes objects seem material.

This is *non-duality*. Vedanta: no seer and no seen—only the seeing.

The second question concerns the relation of one consciousness to another:

If the physical world is inside consciousness, in whose consciousness is it: mine or yours? Who is the lucky one who gets to have the consciousness, and why do all the rest of us have to be figments of his or her imagination? This is a problem that comes up in philosophy 101: the *solipsism*, or the idea that, from the standpoint of each of us individually, the whole world must be an extension of *me*. In the same way we cannot prove the existence of material substance in physical objects, we cannot prove the existence of consciousness in living observers. I don't know, for sure, that "you" are "really there." You say you see things, but *I don't see your seeing*. This is where the distinction between self and consciousness comes in. Modern physics points very strongly in the direction of a unity of consciousness—a singularity of consciousness that is not *me* and not *you*. It cannot be a self. This is very hard for us to realize, especially in the West, because we are not accustomed to thinking this way. We are accustomed to thinking that everything not physical is mental, and that everything mental is self. The paradigm will not shift until we understand the solipsism is a physical absurdity. Consciousness is not self.

Think about it. Self is different from consciousness.

Self is *doing*.

Consciousness is *being*.

Self is thinking, planning, grasping, striving, wanting, loving, hating, laughing, hurting, working, and playing. Self is not life; it is the business of staying alive.

Consciousness is everything.

Without self, nothing ever gets done.

Consciousness is wholeness;

Self seeks wholeness from parts and never finds it. Self is the seeking.

Consciousness is experience.

Self is a "curvature" of experience, a narrowing of focus that creates order within consciousness.

Self is a point of view.

Self is selfish, but not good or bad. Self defines good and bad: Good things keep you warm, dry, fed, entertained, and reproduced. Bad things tend in the opposite direction.

There are many selves. There is one consciousness.

We have always assumed that the experience of being alive is the planning and doing, the wanting and grasping, the working and thinking. We don't think this; we assume it. We do not look deeply into what consciousness is. In the Western tradition, we have discovered great things about the world and how it works, but paid little attention to the direct experience of being alive.

We think of death as the opposite of being alive.

Which brings us to the third question: If consciousness is everything, and there is no universe external to consciousness, what does this say about the meaning of death?

It is the self that dies. You, me, friends, family: everybody dies. Everything dies. How we look, what we do, what we think. It all dies. Time dies. The spirit has no further use for space.

Death is the end of the routine world.

Death is not the end of consciousness.

Consciousness is not in time. It is not after death, or after anything. It doesn't "live on" after death, because it was never in time. Time is in it.

Death is the end of self, the end of a point of view.

How do I know this? I know this because near-death experience is an enigma, a strange happening at a dimensional extreme; near-death is about consciousness, and about light.

The experience of near-death is the experience of being at the edge of the physical world. It is vision beyond space and time. I have certain knowledge, as do many, of the validity of near-death experience. There is no question as to its truth. It is not speculative. Near-death experience happens often, and regularly, and is part of our collective experience. Near-death is a dimensional extreme like the dimensional extremes of modern physics. It is experienced where familiar concepts break down and the limitations of space and time become plain as day. Near-death does not tell us what death is, but it tells us there is more than this world. It tells us what the enigmas of physics tell us: the routine world of coming and going is not all there is.

The twisting, warping, expanding, shrinking, and blending of space, time, and mass of modern physics show that dimensions do not compose a rigid, external world. There is something beyond space, something before time and after time, something more solid than mass. Physics points directly at this truth. Near-death points directly at this truth. We may not know what is beyond, but we do know there is *something* deeper and more fundamental than the physical world.

But, truth be told, I can't say that. It's true, but I can't say it because the words I have used: *beyond, before, after, bigger,* etc., speak of dimensional relations. There can't be anything "before time" or "beyond space" because *before* is a temporal concept, and *beyond* a spatial concept.

Dimensions define *big*, yet they are "inside" something bigger.

Words and meanings become tangled when you try to use dimensional concepts "where" there are no dimensions. Yet—and this is my point—modern physics has shown that space and time are not fundamental and that there is something—if you will forgive the poetic license –"out there," something "on the other side" of space and time.

That something is consciousness! Call it heaven, soul, God, nirvana, being, existence, but don't try to pin it down in words.

We have difficulty grasping what that something is because our most fundamental concepts are based on dimensional relations. To experience directly the greater reality beyond the physical world, and beyond the self, we must transcend dimensions and transcend conceptual understanding based on dimensions. To know, we cannot rely on conceptual knowledge.

We will never make sense of death because it is the making of sense that dies.

We don't know what death is; we can't know; we don't have to know... but we know.

We know, without knowing *about*.

Near-death experience does not fit within the confines of the dimensional world, but that is OK because it no longer has to fit. Modern physics shows that *reality* no longer fits within the dimensional world.

Every near-death experience I know about is an experience of an overpowering sense of peace, of letting go, of joyous acceptance of the wholeness of life, and of profound unconcern for the pieces of life. We hear over and over again, "It didn't seem to matter what happened—whether I lived or died." Or, "I could not understand why everyone was scurrying around the bed trying to bring me back. What was so important?"

Near-death experiences all show that the "me" that wants to do this or have that, the anxiety that makes the unimportant seem important, the leash that leads us about from one errand to the next, the little voice that keeps us pushing and pulling through the day, the *self* we think we *are*, finally comes to rest.

Death is the transcendence of self.

A hospice nurse who is a good friend of mine tells of a young patient she tended for several months before he died. One day, as she came in the door, he greeted her with great excitement. "I know who it is!" he told her. "It's my grandfather! I saw him... in a dream or...I don't know what it was. He was standing there on the other side of a field—a green field—waiting for me. He will be there when I go across."

Another friend of mine is a physician who has been involved with hospice care for thirty-five years. Near-death experiences are a regular feature of his work. Patients routinely report seeing loved ones in the room and speaking with them freely and openly. "She was just sitting there, on the edge of the bed, as she was in life, telling me everything is OK." The message is always, "Everything is OK. It's all right. Don't worry." Recently, a woman under my friend's care spent her last days in complete despondency and withdrawal. Refusing to speak to family, friends, or caretakers about her thoughts or feelings, she seemed to be shriveling away to nothingness. Then, one day, as her breathing became forced and irregular, she sat up in bed suddenly and raised both arms towards the ceiling, smiling ear to ear. Her eyes widened and brightened, staring intently at something beyond her outstretched arms. She held this position for several minutes, then collapsed back into the bed and died.

Death is transcendence of self.

The great religions, in their awkward ways, have been trying to say this for thousands of years.

When my turn comes, I expect to be afraid. I will not know where I am going or what will happen. All the things I have ever done or thought of doing—all the things I have ever said—the things I have written here today—will no longer matter. They will fade to nothingness. There could be pain, or hell, or something much worse than anything I have experienced, or anything I can think of now. But I doubt it. I think everything will be OK. I'm sure of it. I know that whatever happens will be OK. I think the world, and the self that is me, will simply evaporate. It will be like waking from a dream... or, like being born...

When I die, I will be dead.

I'm scared, and I can't wait!

SAMUEL AVERY

Samuel Avery holds degrees from Oberlin College and University of Kentucky. He has taught university courses in American History, European History, and American Government. Avery has practiced meditation daily for over forty-five years. He also has written a number of books (and audio books) on the relationship of physics and consciousness to each other, including *Buddha and the Quantum*; *Transcendence of the Western Mind*; and *The Dimensional Structure of Consciousness*.

CPSIA information can be obtained
at www.ICGtesting.com
Printed in the USA
BVOW08s0719111117
500065BV00002B/78/P